At the Jazz Band Ball

PHILIP OAKES

At the
Jazz Band Ball

a memory of the 1950s

The past exudes legend: one can't make pure
clay of time's mud. There is no life that can be
recaptured wholly; as it was. Which is to say
that all biography is ultimately fiction. What
does that tell you about the nature of life, and
does one really want to know?

Dubin's Lives: Bernard Malamud

In truth I seem to have felt mostly the joys of living; in remembering, in recording, thanks to
the gift of the Muse, it is the pain.

Notebooks: Robert Lowell

ANDRE DEUTSCH

For the last time, for my children

First published 1983 by
André Deutsch Limited
105 Great Russell Street, WC1

Typeset by Falcon Graphic Art Ltd
Wallington, Surrey
Printed in Great Britain by
Mackays of Chatham Ltd

One

WE MADE LOVE standing up in the front porch of Sadie's digs. It was the last winter of the war and there were no lamps lit in the street. Across Highbury Fields came the hum of machinery from the factory which made radio parts and beyond the trees, trolley buses rolled like dim lanterns towards the West End.

It was bitterly cold. The front of Sadie's thighs were like marble and I could feel a draught working its way beneath my shirt and up the small of my back. It didn't matter. The discomfort was of no importance. We were joined in a liquid heat which burned away all other considerations. I could hear my breath soughing moistly in Sadie's hair and my forehead bumped against the tiled wall.

There was a mat on the floor of the porch and as it began a slow skid towards the opposite wall I kicked it away. We were bolted together on a runaway train. There could be no obstructions, nothing to slow it down. Sadie's fingers dug into my shoulders. She wailed into my ear and it was the last sound in the world. We left the track, soaring through darkness and silence into a cave where small sounds became more insistent until they could be identified as traffic and rain, the familiar mutter of London by night. I was so tired I could hardly stand. I seemed to have travelled a great distance with someone I hardly knew. Sadie sighed and I stroked her hair. 'Are you all right?' I asked.

'Frozen.'

'Let's go and get a coffee.'

'They don't serve just coffee. You have to buy something to eat as well.'

1

'We'll have something to eat then.'

'I don't fancy it,' she said, 'It's not worth the money.'

She was right, of course. We had already had supper in the café at Highbury Barn. Vienna steak and chips, with fruit salad to follow. Before that we had been to the cinema at Finsbury Park to see *Fanny by Gaslight*. It was our regular Saturday night routine and making love was the best part of it. But, once it was over, even that was unsatisfactory. It was a habit into which we had both fallen, as if the act of love had inevitably to follow a declaration of love, whatever the inconvenience, whatever the consequences.

Somehow, we felt, it was expected of us. We had first met years before at the Methodist Homes in Lancashire where we had exchanged promises like prisoners sustaining ourselves with glimpses of the future until our release. We had talked yearningly of marriage and of having our own home, as if by imagining an ideal we could equip ourselves for it. The truth was that neither of us was remotely suited to live with the other. Sadie's laugh, a shrill whinny which she would emit without cause or warning, got on my nerves. She, in turn, thought the poems I was beginning to write were either embarrassing or obscure. We clung to each other like survivors after a shipwreck, not daring to let go in case the water instantly engulfed us. Old loyalties kept us afloat, but they were coming apart.

Already there was daylight between us. I was nearly seventeen and in a year's time I would be called up for my national service. My mother, a housebound invalid in the Potteries, wrote to me once or twice a week urging me to return home where I could look after her. Sadie felt that she was being passed by, but what aggravated her most was knowing that next spring I was going to become a father.

In my last year at the Homes I had formed an attachment to Sister Emma, the house mother. Sadie was already in London and it was with Emma that I had first made love. She was fifteen years older than me and when she took me into her bed it had been an act of kindness rather than passion. The affair was over by the time I left the Homes. We had made no plans, beyond promising to keep in touch, and when she had visited me one day in London and told me that she was pregnant I had been panic-stricken. My newly-won freedom was about to be snatched away, my plans for a career threatened. I could understand Emma's predicament and I despised myself for not wanting to share it. But what had happened between us seemed so distant in time and place that it might have been enacted by two different people. I could not recognise myself. I was no longer the schoolboy that I had been then, but I was not yet a man. The thought of responsibility appalled me. I tried to imagine what my mother would say and my desperation doubled. Emma took my hand. 'We'll manage somehow,' she said, 'you mustn't worry.' And, without wanting to know more, I believed her.

Emma's composure had always been reassuring, but now her courage and resourcefulness amazed me. She quit the Homes and found a job as a housekeeper with a family in Surrey. She told them she was pregnant and was assured that, with or without a child, she could stay with them for as long as she liked. 'It'll do for the time being,' she said. 'Until I get myself sorted out.'

I felt comforted, but my conscience pricked in another direction. I felt obliged to tell Sadie.

'You're joking!' she said.

'I'm not. Honestly.'

'You mean Sister Emma that I knew? We're talking about the same person?'

'It was after you'd come to London. I was on my own.'

'Not for long,' said Sadie. She shook her head as if she was trying to rid herself of a great weight. 'I can't believe it. The two of you carrying on like that with no one knowing about it.'

'They mustn't know now,' I said. 'You're not to tell anyone.'

'I'm not likely to. Where d'you suppose it leaves us?'

It was a question I had hoped to avoid. 'What do you mean?'

'All this talk about us getting married. You've got other things to think of now.'

'It doesn't follow. Nothing's changed,' I said, knowing as I spoke that everything had indeed changed.

'What about maintenance? How are you going to pay that?'

'We've not discussed it yet.'

'How about your mother?'

'She's not to be told.'

'Have you thought about adoption?'

'Emma wouldn't want that.'

Sadie digested the information. 'Then I suppose it's up to her.'

'I suppose it is.'

'Think yourself lucky,' said Sadie. 'You've got away with it this time.'

She never brought the subject up again. It was as though she realised that however volatile the facts might be, Emma was the stopper in the bottle. They would never escape or explode. Everything was taken care of. What Sadie could not countenance was that I had made love to Emma while still writing her weekly letters in which I repeated the ritual vows, made stale by constant repetition. The words were worn smooth. They no longer had purchase or potency, but to Sadie they constituted a spell which I had broken. 'You were telling lies,' she said. 'I can't believe anything you say.'

'And what were you doing.' I demanded. 'You're not telling me you didn't go out with other boys before I came down.'

'Men, not boys.'

'And what did you do with them?'

'Nothing to be ashamed of. They were just friends.'

'You never mentioned them in your letters.'

'That makes two of us.'

Honours were far from even, but there was blame on both sides and we avoided further argument. It would have been too exhausting as we lived less than a mile from each other. Sadie had a bed-sit with an elderly widow who gave her a key only on her promise that she would be indoors before midnight. I had a room in a boarding-house run by two sisters named Minnie and Lily who wore identical green baize dresses and lived in the basement. A flourishing spider plant masked their window, but occasionally they could be glimpsed behind it squinting up at the front door in case any of their lodgers attempted to smuggle a woman into the house. They had always maintained an all-male establishment. Even the wives of their long-established lodgers – mostly civil servants and commercial travellers who stayed in London during the week – would be admitted only by special arrangement. Except for themselves, they had decided that women were unclean and they were fanatical in their determination to keep them on the pavement where they belonged.

About a week after I moved in my neighbour on the top floor, a civil engineer from Bilston, brought back a girl from his office. It was nearly midnight and the house seemed to be asleep. It was in the middle of a tall Georgian terrace. My windows looked out on to the tops of trees and pigeons squatted on the sill. It was remarkably quiet; all the street noises were filtered through a mesh of branches and leaves. The only disturbance from within was the spasmodic flushing of the bathroom lavatory on the second floor. That and another WC on the floor below it served the whole house and I was on my way downstairs after a particularly sustained flush signalled that the bathroom was free when there was pandemonium.

The lights in the hall and the stair-well suddenly went on. Halfway up the stairs, their shoes in their hands, I saw my neighbour and his girl. Below them, frozen by the blaze of electricity like athletes in a flash-bulb photograph, were Minnie and Lily. They had sprung from the basement where they had been lying in wait, and with their hands extended like claws, raced up the stairs. The girl screamed as they grabbed her by the hair, but still hung on to her shoes. My neighbour tried to intervene, but was thrown to one side. Doors opened on each landing and heads looked out to witness the extraordinary spectacle of our landladies, their faces crimson and their sleeves rolled up to their elbows, bundling a much younger woman downstairs. It was like seeing a rabbit mauled by a pair of terriers. When they reached the hall Minnie flung open the front door while Lily kept hold of the girl's hair. Then both of them seized her arms and threw her down the steps and into the street. Her coat sagged open, her blouse hung out of her skirt and her hair stood on end, but she still clutched her shoes.

My neighbour raised a quivering hand. 'There's no need for this violence.'

'There'll be more if you're not gone within ten minutes,' promised Minnie.

None of us doubted that she meant what she said. The lodger left, bags in hand, and the lights were extinguished within a quarter of an hour. By the end of the week his room had been let to a young librarian named Barrett who made the exhilarating discovery that the house three doors down was a girl's remand home and that from his balcony he had an uninterrupted view of the garden where they lay sunbathing. All that summer we blew kisses through the rose trellises and laburnams that lay between us until the warden of the home complained.

That evening we found the window nailed shut and the balcony declared out of bounds. It was not safe, said Minnie. She did not want to be responsible for any accidents.

The house rules were strict but we did not complain. In wartime London, Minnie and Lily gave good value for money. For thirty shillings a week they provided a shabby but comfortable room, a substantial breakfast and an evening meal. There was a lounge with a coal fire and a billiard-table, bald in patches but still serviceable. Sheets were changed once a week, so was the hand-towel. I had a writing-table and a chair and a wash-stand equipped with a flowered basin and a jug of cold water. Laundry was our own concern and on my mother's insistence I sent a parcel of dirty clothes home every Friday.

For her it represented a moral triumph. When I first moved into lodgings I had taken my laundry to Sadie's digs where she had a plentiful supply of hot water. 'It's not right,' said my mother when she found out. 'I don't like to think of her washing your underthings. It's not decent.'

No argument that I could muster would change her mind. It was bad enough that I was not living at home; what was intolerable was the thought of another woman being admitted to intimacies which she was denied. My mother had never met Sadie but in spite, or possibly because, of my glowing descriptions she disliked her. We knew nothing about her background, she complained. What was she doing living alone in London? Had she no family to go to? I did my best to explain that we had met on equal terms in identical circumstances and that we both wanted to live independent lives. But it was useless. Sadie was an outsider. She belonged to another tribe. She was up to no good.

My mother had an almost mystical view of her own family. Perfect communion existed between all its members and no stranger could possibly match the standards they set. As my mother's health deteriorated and she became physically more frail she looked back on her youth as a golden age in which no one was needy or sick or ignoble and whose representatives (her brothers, sisters and cousins) were beyond reproach. Her housekeeper, Mary Evans, did not share her delusion. But she knew better than to question it. 'Show some sense,' she told me, 'don't upset her any more than you have to.'

Implicitly she acknowledged that some upset was inevitable. Mary had been with my mother since the day she returned from hospital after an operation to remove a tumour from her brain. In the nine years they had lived together Mary's gilt hair had turned grey and my mother's paralysis, a direct consequence of the operation which had saved her life, had worsened. She also suffered from occasional bouts of epilepsy, but somehow she felt them to be degrading and always referred to them dismissively as 'my attacks'. It was Mary who accompanied me to the Bluecoat School at Wolverhampton when I was sent to board there at the age of eight and it was Mary who welcomed me back home when I was expelled five years later. She had gone with me to buy my first pair of long trousers when, without warning, I was despatched to the orphanage in Lancashire. And she had told me that I was right to go to London instead of returning home as my mother wished.

'You're best away,' she said. 'She won't like it, but you'd go potty if you stayed here. There's nowt for you to do. You've grown up somewhere else. You don't belong.'

Mary had seen what my mother refused to acknowledge. I had left home before I was old enough to put down roots. My first friends had found other companions. I had forgotten the passwords and the rituals of my boyhood. My family meant nothing to me, nor did the place. Once arrived, I longed to be gone.

I could not say precisely what I wanted to do or where I wanted to be. But London seemed far enough away for me to escape the worst of my mother's reproaches and it was where I thought I might find an opening as a journalist. I had never considered any other profession. At school my best subjects had always been History and English. I had written reports and poems for school magazines as well as circulating a broadsheet of scandal and rumour which we laboriously duplicated with the aid of a John Bull printing set. My heroes were men like Negley Farson and Vernon Bartlett, travellers and prophets, who wrote wisely and well and who were, above all, citizens of the world. I admired their fluency and envied their freedom. In my imagination they merged with reporters I had seen in films – laconic, hard-drinking, uniformed in trench-coats and snap-brimmed fedoras – and I wanted to be like them. How the transformation could be achieved I had no idea, but it seemed less likely to happen in the Potteries than in London where Fleet Street lay and where Sadie was already installed.

For three months I lived in a hostel and worked as an office-boy while I studied shorthand and typing. I found it impossible to read my notes back and I could not understand how the typewriter keys with which I fumbled beneath a bib of black cotton produced, not the exercises I was meant to copy, but lines of jabberwocky. I tried to imitate the crisp rhythms laid down by the typing instructor, but they were as difficult to follow as the steps of the tango we were learning in the ballroom-dancing classes I had also joined. Sadie was both a proficient typist and a good dancer and I despaired that she could do so easily what I found intractable.

'Just relax,' she said. 'Don't try so hard.'

'I am relaxed.'

She shook her head. 'No you're not. Stop thinking about it in advance and let it come naturally.'

I did as she advised. My typing improved and I began to enjoy the dancing more. Every Wednesday evening the class met in the basement of the hostel where I lived. We had a wooden parquet floor and a gramophone with a selection of Victor Sylvester records. Nothing more was needed, said the instructor, all we had to do was feel the music. We swayed and spun to *Jealousy* as if we were tethered to a length of elastic and as we came together I could feel Sadie's breasts moulding my chest as they did when we made love.

'You're standing too close,' she said.

'We're meant to be close. That's what they told us.'

'Not this close,' said Sadie. 'I can't breathe.'

She straightened her arms and pushed me away. As she did so a gust of her perfume eddied between us and I sniffed it greedily before it went to waste. We reversed perfectly and Sadie leaned back in my arms so that her pony-tail almost brushed the floor. I managed to hang on and hauled her upright as the dance ended.

She dug her nails into the palm of my hand. 'Keep it up and we'll be putting in for our bronze soon.'

I had no desire for any kind of medal, but it was satisfying to learn a dance as tricky as the tango and I wished that everything else in life would come together so neatly. There were so many loose ends. Eventually, I supposed, I would master shorthand and typing. But what I would do then I could not begin to imagine.

One week brought two possibilities. The Headmasters' Association arranged an interview with the News Editor of *The Daily Sketch* and the next day I received a letter from a friend of Emma's named Sally Derby offering to introduce me to a sub-editor on *The News Chronicle*. Sally was a pacifist and her house in Tottenham was a meeting point for every kind of dissident. Going there for tea one afternoon I had met a homosexual actor, several Quakers and an anarchist poet who had registered as a conscientious objector and volunteered to work in the mines.

'And what will you do?' he asked.

'Go in the army I suppose.'

'Is that what you want to do?'

'I don't really mind,' I said. 'I don't want to kill anyone.'

'Or be killed.'

'Of course not.'

'It's possible,' he said. 'Don't ever lose sight of that. It's not just a moral issue. You could be saving your own skin by refusing to fight.'

No pacifist I had ever met had put the argument to me like that before. It seemed engagingly cynical. 'Is that why you're a CO?' I asked.

'Partly. And I hate bloody uniforms. Anyhow, it might all have been a waste of time. We had a doodle-bug

in the next street yesterday. Two houses completely flattened. I'm off to Scotland tomorrow.'

The V1 and V2 rockets, which the newspapers had
dubbed doodle-bugs, were being aimed at London from
launching ramps on the French coast. No one could guess
where they were likely to fall. Hearing one overhead
when the engine cut out was a sickening experience.
I had developed the habit of counting aloud as if I could
somehow distance the bomb by intoning numbers. If
I reached eight before it exploded there had been no
real danger. A count of five meant that the rocket had
fallen within half a mile. Walking home one night Sadie
and I had watched one chug overhead, trailing a plume
of red sparks like a firework. The engine stopped and
against the starlight we actually saw it stagger and fall.
It disappeared behind the rooftops and there was a flash,
followed by a muffled explosion, as if the houses between
us had soaked up the blast saturating their bricks and
mortar with heat and light.

Veterans of the London blitz assured me that I had
missed the worst of it and I believed them. There was
no doubt that the war in Europe was drawing to an
end and the rockets seemed as futile as they were
frightening. I was much more concerned about the possibility of being sent to fight in the Far East. I imagined
jungles swarming with leeches and savage yellow soldiers
who would rather die than surrender. When I professed
to be unworried about being called-up I was telling only
half the truth. Time, I believed, was on my side but,
almost as an act of faith or superstition, I felt that by
establishing myself as a civilian with a job and an identity
which lay outside the war, I was presenting my credentials for survival. I never considered who would read
them, but it was important that they should be on file.

Sally was helpful but vague. She had no idea what the
man on *The News Chronicle* could do but said that I should
show him samples of my work. I was grateful but ap-

prehensive. Nothing I had written was good enough for print, so I kept the appointment taking with me a sheaf of badly typed poems in a loose-leaf binder. It was a Saturday morning in early autumn. There was a smell of bonfires in the air, but as I walked from Southgate station through rows of trim suburban houses, sunlight glared unseasonably from the snowcemmed walls. They were all painted white and had rounded corners like pictures I had seen of ocean liners. The sub-editor was sitting cross-legged on his lawn with a motor mower spread around him in oily sections.

'D'you know anything about these things?' he asked.

I shook my head. 'I'm hopeless with machines.'

'Pity.' He scratched his nose and left a black smear. 'Sally tells me you write poetry.'

I offered him the binder. 'I've got some here.'

'Waste of time,' said the sub-editor. 'Poetry's got nothing to do with journalism. If that's what you want to do, stay away from newspapers.'

'But I'm looking for a job.'

'Find something else,' he said. 'If you're any kind of writer, find another line of work. I mean it. Writers don't belong in newspapers. They think words are something precious. Their feelings get hurt.'

'What about you?' I asked.

The sub-editor looked gleeful. 'I'm not a writer. All I do is muck about with what other people write.'

'Do they mind?'

'Of course they mind,' said the sub-editor. 'They scream bloody murder. Not that they know what they're talking about. It's just their pride that's hurt. What I do is polish their frightful prose. They ought to be grateful.'

'Maybe some of them are.'

The sub-editor selected a spark-plug and held it out for my inspection. 'Show me one reporter who doesn't believe that he knows best and I'll turn this into pure gold.'

'I don't know any reporters,' I said. 'I just want to be one.'

The sub-editor put down the plug and wiped his hands. 'You don't listen, do you. I've offered my best advice and you ignore it. What else can I tell you?'

'Who could I go and see?' I thought it advisable not to mention *The Daily Sketch*. *The News Chronicle* was a much superior paper and I did not want to invite another burst of professional scorn.

The sub-editor picked a handful of daisies and slowly began to string them into a chain. 'All right then,' he said at last. 'There's a man I know called Eric Sly. He runs a small news agency. Covers police courts mostly. I know he's short-staffed at present. You could give him a ring.' He raised a warning finger as I started to thank him. 'It may come to nothing. It's just on the off-chance. Don't say I didn't warn you.'

He gave me the telephone number and I rang it five minutes later from the underground station. The voice that answered was loud and high-pitched as if Mr Sly was either deaf or tone-deaf. 'Hello, hello,' he shouted. 'Sly's Reporting Service here.'

I told him who I was and why I had called. 'I gather you might have a vacancy,' I said.

There was a moment's pause followed by a peculiar whooping sound that levelled into a hum and I understood that Mr Sly was laughing. It was a mannerism with which I was to become familiar. What it signalled was indecision and embarrassment, but hearing it for the first time I thought the line must be faulty. 'Hello,' I said, 'can you hear me?'

'I can hear you,' he said, 'but there's been a mistake. There's no vacancy. I mean there's no job to *be* vacant. I'm on my own.'

I was about to apologise for troubling him when he continued. 'To be perfectly frank, I did have a partner. But he's in the army now and there's no way of knowing when he'll be back. Of course, the income's gone down as I've had to reduce the coverage. But if we produced more reports perhaps we could afford someone else in the office. And that would mean that the service was more efficient.'

He stopped for breath, but I said nothing. Incomprehensibly to me, Mr Sly was reviewing the situation – something, I discovered, that he frequently did – and all I could do was await his conclusion. It took him several minutes to reach it. I learned that the agency covered proceedings at two magistrates' courts at Clerkenwell and North London and that he supplied reports to the daily, evening and local papers as well as to the Press Association and Exchange Telegraph. He himself was based at Clerkenwell and a reporter from *The Hackney Gazette* attended to national stories which might break at North London. 'He's very reliable,' said Mr Sly, 'but his real interest is boxing. It's not entirely satisfactory.'

I thought I glimpsed an opening. 'Perhaps there is a vacancy then.'

Mr Sly hummed loudly. 'It's the lack of experience,' he said. 'Court reporting's reponsible work. You need to be able to take a good note. Besides which, I don't think you're old enough.'

'Does that matter? I won't tell anyone.'

'It's the law,' he said testily. 'I doubt whether you'd be covered by insurance if there was a libel action.'

It was a possibility which had not occurred to me. Working for Mr Sly had complications which multiplied by the minute. 'And there are the lavatories,' he said. 'I don't have the proper toilet facilities for staff.'

'I beg your pardon?'

'The premises are not my own,' he said. 'They're borrowed.'

It was a curious expression, I thought. 'Could I come and see you?' I asked.

There was a brief burst of humming. 'I don't see why not,' said Mr Sly. 'But not here.'

'Not where?'

'I'm at home, not the office. That's where you've called me. Someone else is looking after things today.'

I decided not to ask who. 'How about Monday?' I suggested.

'I think I could manage that.'

'What time would be convenient?'

'Not after four,' said Mr Sly. 'They lock the doors then.'

'Who locks the doors?'

'The police,' he said, as if the question itself was absurd.

'What's the address?'

Mr Sly gave me careful instructions how to find Clerkenwell Magistrates Court. 'I shall be by the front entrance at a quarter to four,' he said. 'Try to be on time.'

The court was in King's Cross Road, not far from Mount Pleasant Post Office, an area I had already explored while looking for the places described by Arnold Bennett in his novel, *Riceyman's Steps*. The steps were still there sloping back from the pavement and as I walked up and down them I remembered Bennett's tombstone, a dagger of black marble which cast its shadow across my father's more modest grave in Burslem cemetery. They had been in the same class at school and as soon as I had confessed to wanting to become a writer my mother had invoked Bennett as the example I should follow. Not his private life, she emphasised; there had been that business with the French woman and it was well known that he drank, a failing which my teetotal family could not tolerate. His industry, though, was admirable and to ensure that I bore it in mind I was presented with his book *How To Live On Twenty-Four Hours A Day*. I sampled the first two chapters but found them nagging and dull, as I did most good advice. It was difficult to believe that the man who had lived such a scandalous life could write so boringly.

Especially, I reminded myself, when there were so many interesting things to write about. Almost opposite the steps there was a Rowton House, built of red brick, with turrets flying metal flags and windows like embrasures. It resembled a medieval castle. Iron railings surrounded it and the wide entrance deserved a drawbridge. Through the railings I looked down into the basement rooms where the ceilings were striped with neon tubes and newspapers hung from brackets on the walls. Already men were queueing up to book their night's lodging. They squatted on their haunches and smoked cigarettes held in their cupped hands. 'Seen everything?' demanded one of them as I sauntered by.

Not enough, I wanted to reply. But I was not looking for trouble. The truth was that I was curious about everyone and everything. I imagined people's lives as Chinese water flowers, each of them locked within its shell, but blossoming exotically when submerged in an acquarium. The comparison was incomplete. In time the flowers became saturated and fell apart, but people went on changing. One revelation succeeded another. There was no limit to what I might learn and understand.

I hurried on towards the court. The building was easy to recognise and from across the road I saw a man I had no doubt was Mr Sly. He wore large, perfectly round spectacles and a shiny grey suit with trouser bottoms which ended above his ankles. There was a gap of at least an inch between his shirt collar and his throat and when he turned his head I was reminded of a tortoise, swivelling freely within its shell. In one hand he held several sheets of typescript and as he read them he plucked at his hair with the inky fingers of his free hand until it stood up on end. A bicycle clip clasped one spindly calf and his toes met each other at an angle of ninety degrees. 'Come in, come in,' he said as I went to meet him, 'they want to lock up.'

We dodged into the entrance hall where a police sergeant stood waiting. 'Let's be having you,' he said.

Mr Sly giggled nervously. 'Better in than out.'

'Not all of them think that,' said the sergeant, 'as you very well know. We've had one or two make a dash for it.'

'Did any of them get away?' I asked.

The sergeant slapped a heavy key into the palm of his hand. 'There was a bloke cut and run when they were taking him to the van. Straight across the yard and over the wall. Except he didn't get over it. There was barbed wire on the top.' He sucked air through a gap in his front teeth. 'Very nasty. You should get Mr Sly to tell you about it.'

I was led away but the sergeant called after me: 'Remember the song, *Hanging on the Old Barbed Wire?*' He whistled a few bars as he slammed the front door and turned the key.

'We go this way,' said Mr Sly, steering me down a panelled corridor and through an office where another sergeant stood writing in a ledger and a constable was making tea. They both looked up and nodded as we hurried past them into what looked like a white tiled catacomb lined with green metal doors. 'Here we are,' said Mr Sly, and pushed one of the doors open. The room was quite bare except for a small filing cabinet, two chairs and a desk on which stood a typewriter. A single bulb burned behind a metal grille over the door and the window was barred. I realised that Mr Sly's office was a cell.

'It's not quite the Ritz,' he said.

'It's very handy.'

He nodded vigorously. 'It's certainly that. Living over the shop, so to speak.'

'How long have you been here?'

'Six months or so. We came to an arrangement.' He looked around him with evident satisfaction. 'I keep thinking I might put a carpet on the floor. But it isn't really worth it. I mean, it's not my place. Not officially. You don't think it's important, do you?'

'Not a bit.'

'That's what I thought.' He waved me towards a chair. 'Sit down and tell me about yourself.'

I told Mr Sly the story of my life. I told him that I had always wanted to be a journalist, that I was learning shorthand and typing and that I understood the need for total accuracy. I did not tell him that I wrote poetry. In that dingy cell whose walls were yellowed like old piano keys it seemed irrelevant.

'What's your shorthand speed?' he asked.

'Eighty,' I said, as confidently as I could. 'It'll be up

to a hundred and twenty soon.'

'Sometimes we need verbatim.'

'I could probably manage.'

He looked doubtful. 'What I really want is someone to phone copy through to the papers. The three evenings pay a retainer and so do the agencies. We try to let them have the story as it happens. Then we deliver finished copy to the dailies by hand.'

'Where's the telephone?'

'Ah,' said Mr Sly, 'that's the problem. We have to find a box that's free. Sometimes it's difficult. People don't understand that news is urgent.'

'I suppose not.'

'Then there's copy for the locals. We have a filing system which tells you which papers cover which district and it's important to work out the right number of carbons. If you fall short the whole thing has to be typed out again.' He picked up a sheet of carbon paper and held it to the light. It was perforated from top to bottom to the consistency of lace. 'It's heavy typing, I'm afraid,' he said. 'Do you think you can read my writing?'

He showed me a report written in bold and clear script on a pad of copy paper. 'My mother writes a bit like that,' I told him. 'She calls it blackboard writing.'

He nodded his approval. 'We can't afford to make mistakes.'

'I'd try not to make any.' Secretly I was appalled by what sounded like a routine of unrelieved drudgery, but I resolved to press on. 'Would I be able to do any reporting? On my own, I mean.'

'Eventually. You might be sorry when you do. Crime isn't at all glamorous. Some of it's sordid and almost all of it is boring.'

'But it's what you do.'

'Ah, yes. Well.' Mr Sly groped behind him and scratched between his buttocks with complete absorption. 'For me it's a business. I'm not looking for excitement.'

'What about wages?'

'Three pounds, ten shilling a week,' he said. 'That's fifteen shillings more than a trainee's rate. If you come to work here, that is. Do you want to?'

'I think so.'

'Think it over for a few days. The snag from my point of view is that you'll be called up just as you've learned to be useful.' He smiled ruefully. 'Frankly, you're not a good investment. Let's give it to the end of the week. You can tell me then if you want to come and I'll say if I want you.'

'Right you are,' I said. I realised that Mr Sly was more astute than he at first appeared, but I did not guess the extent of his reputation. I learned that the next day when I went to see the News Editor of *The Daily Sketch*. He was a plump Scot with fair, thinning hair and a face as pink as boiled ham. 'You'd work as a copy boy,' he told me without preamble. 'That means you'd go on a job with a reporter and phone his copy through to the office.'

'I want to learn reporting itself.'

'Of course you do, laddie. That's what they all want. But it takes time.' He massaged his jowls and sighed. 'You wouldn't stand a chance but for the war. We've got no grown men. That's why we're taking on babies.'

He spoke entirely without malice. It was as though he was explaining a truth which should have been self-evident. I had never met anyone so worldly. He wore a cream silk shirt and a red and blue striped tie and I could smell his cologne through the reek of oil and printers' ink which suffused the building. I was deeply impressed but I felt bound to challenge him. 'I've already been offered a job,' I said.

'Have you now? By a newspaper?'

'By an agency.'

'And which would that be?'

I showed him Mr Sly's visiting card and he picked up one of his telephones. 'What do we know about a stringer called Sly?' he enquired. 'Covers police courts and that.' There was an instant reply and he put the phone down. 'You're lucky,' he said. 'He's a good man. One of our better connections. Gave us a story about someone in the dock shooting at the magistrate. What's he going to pay you?'

'Three pounds ten.'

'We'd pay you three pounds. There's a job if you want it.'

I admired his silk shirt and thought how impressive it would be to say I worked for *The Daily Sketch*. And I thought of Mr Sly in his tarnished cell and how – for only ten shillings a week more – I might soon be typing his copy. The money was important, but what it signified was more important still. Even with my meagre qualifications, Mr Sly thought I was worth it.

'Thanks all the same,' I said. 'I think I'll be better off at Sly's.'

The News Editor gave me a hard look. 'It's really fixed up, is it?'

'Almost. We're letting each other know.'

'Good luck then, off you go.' He did not get up from his desk but nodded me goodbye. 'It it doesn't work out you can get in touch. I won't hold it against you.'

I waited until Thursday and then wrote to Mr Sly saying that after considering all that he had said I wanted to join him. He did not telephone me the next day as I had expected, but on Saturday morning there was a manila envelope beside my breakfast plate. I slit it open with my bread-knife and read the letter as slowly as I could. It was worth taking time over. The job was mine. I was to become a trainee reporter with Eric R. Sly's Court Reporting Service Ltd, at the salary agreed, and I would start work in a fortnight's time.

There was a post-script. 'Sorry about the typing. As you will no doubt appreciate, the ribbon on this machine has seen better days.'

Two

MR SLY told me to call him Eric. 'We're a very informal office,' he explained, 'there's no need to stand on ceremony.' His routine, though, was rigid and I soon learned to conform to it. I got to the court shortly after nine o'clock, entering the building by the back door and passing through the yard described with such relish by the sergeant I had met on my first day. He was a warrant officer named Searle. 'Did you see the wire?' he asked me when we met again. 'Get old Sly to tell you about it.'

As it transpired there was no need. Several other policemen including the assistant jailer, a constable named Croft whose waxed moustache formed perfect right angles with the pillar of his neck, described in bloody detail the occasion when a runaway prisoner attempting to scale the wall had fallen and hung screaming from the barbs surmounting it.

PC Croft and the jailer, Sergeant Mackintosh, prepared the charge sheets for the day and my first job was to copy the details. The business of the court began at ten o'clock with the magistrate hearing applications for summonses, and the first prisoner entered the dock half an hour later. The court itself reminded me of a chapel or a theatre. It was panelled in oak. The magistrate's chair was upholstered in scarlet leather and from his padded throne he looked down into the well of the court in which solicitors were cooped and on to the counsel's bench to their right, with the press bench behind it. The dock was an iron cage, waist high, standing directly beneath the glass dome of the roof. It was in front of the public gallery where I soon began to recognise familiar faces, men and women who attended court every day in search of drama or entertainment.

21

They could easily be distinguished from friends or relatives of the defendants by their sporting attitude to the proceedings. They were students of form who followed particular magistrates and debated the finer points of their favourite crimes. Brothel-keeping always drew a good house. So did rape, housebreaking and grievous bodily harm. But even minor transgressions such as loitering with intent or soliciting earned the occasional murmur of applause as points were scored and allegations denied. No irony from the bench went unacknowledged; no tale of police villainy lacked its due response.

The previous year, Eric told me, one of the spectators had narrowly escaped injury when a man in the dock had drawn a revolver from his pocket and fired at the magistrate. The assistant jailer had wrestled the gun from his hand, but several shots had gone wild. One had furrowed the edge of the press box. Another had splintered the wall behind the public gallery.

'I heard about that,' I said. 'And you told me that court reporting wasn't exciting.'

Eric counted on his fingers. 'It's the most excitement I've had in five years.'

'Were you scared?'

'Not really,' he said. 'It made us a lot of money.'

He lived in constant hope that such a thing might happen again. No case, however trivial, could be safely ignored. Eric had learned to expect the unexpected.

From ten-thirty until the court rose for lunch he sat in the press box, taking notes and scribbling stories which I would take away to type. In the afternoons he would transcribe the remainder of his case load while I kept watch in court, dimly aware of clouds cruising over the dirty glass dome and the tick of the clock reverberating within sheets of oak. Even on Thursday afternoons when matrimonial cases were heard and reporting was restricted to a summary of events and the magistrate's decision, Eric insisted that I should maintain my vigil.

'Something might happen,' he insisted and although it never did, my knowledge of the barrens of human nature was painfully extended. I heard women crying as they described being beaten and betrayed. I learned about poverty and sickness; about bankrupt marriages and the end of hope. After a month I wanted no more of it.

'It's not as if there was any copy,' I complained. 'It's just misery and I can't write about it anyway.'

'For practice you could,' said Eric.

'Matrimonial's a waste of time. Let me do some of the other stuff. Just the little stories. You don't want to be bothered with them.'

He allowed himself to be persuaded and I began to cover the lower end of the list: petty theft, assault and squabbles between neighbours. My first published report – a woman convicted of stealing from her gas meter – appeared in *The St Pancras Chronicle*. I cut it out and kept it in my wallet for weeks.

My main job, though, was simply to process the flow of news. Each day I telephoned *The Star*, *The Evening Standard* and *The Evening News* repeating the same story to relays of languid copy-takers until my ears ached and the words became gibberish. I typed reports for the locals, frequently miscalculating the number of papers which covered each district, so that I had to type the piece again. And, late in the afternoon, I delivered the pick of the day's stories to the nationals. It was something to look forward to. I caught the bus along Farringdon Road to the bottom of Fleet Street and plotted my way like a postman: to the *Daily Express* first, then the *Daily Telegraph*, across the street to the Press Association, back again for the *Daily Mirror*, down Bouverie Street to the *News Chronicle* and *Daily Mail* and up Queen Victoria Street to the Exchange Telegraph. I never got beyond the main entrance. The envelope containing our copy was received by a commissionaire, blazing with campaign medals, after which it would disappear into some inner recess where lights flashed and machinery hummed.

I often loitered, hoping to see famous faces. But the glamour of the building was usually enough to feed my dreams. There was so much marble and plate glass; lifts went up and down, disgorging men in cashmere coats with briefcases bulging beneath their arms. They were saluted by the commissionaires who dispatched messenger boys on urgent errands with a snap of their fingers. It was exciting to think that stories which I had helped to prepare were being digested by organisations so sophisticated and important. We were helping to feed them; we were of use. We were part of the industry.

But money was a problem. After paying my rent I had little over thirty shillings left each week to buy a midday meal and take Sadie out on Saturday night. I allowed myself five cigarettes a day. I economised on fares, walking to work when it was fine and frequently covering the delivery round on foot in order to pocket what I saved. By Wednesday I was broke and had to ask Eric for a sub. Paying in advance went against all his principles. 'It doesn't solve the problem,' he would say, counting out coins from the purse he kept in his hip pocket. 'Next week it'll be just the same. You must learn to live within your means.'

Eric was a Quaker, a non-smoker and a teetotaller who spent practically nothing on himself. But he was committed to good works, rallies and appeals to which he gave both time and money. He was unlike any journalist that the police at the court had known. He did not swear. He did not tell dirty jokes. He was deeply offended when a detective intimated it would be worth his while not to report the prosecution of a local shopkeeper for receiving stolen groceries.

'It took me a while to understand what he was suggesting,' he told me later. 'He was actually offering me a bribe.'

There was an innocence about Eric which had survived all his years of court reporting and which gave him immunity from the innuendo and jokes aimed at him. I was more vulnerable. In the jailer's office it was assumed that I was a virgin and each day began with a ritual interrogation by PC Croft.

'How did you get on last night, then?'

'All right.'

'Only all right? Tell us the truth lad. Have you dipped your wick yet?'

Anticipating the question my response was always the same. I would smile cryptically and attend to the charge sheets. I behaved like a prisoner under caution. It was unwise to give information which, without doubt, would be used against me.

Sometimes, however, there was no defence. One morning Sergeant Mackintosh asked me to pass him a roll of banknotes, secured by an elastic band, which lay on the far side of his desk. 'Drop it in here,' he said, holding open a foolscap envelope and when I did so, he grinned broadly.

'Have you any idea where that money's been?'

'Not a clue.'

'It was in Polly Adams' purse,' said the sergeant.

Polly was a King's Cross prostitute who was arrested, on average, once or twice a month. She was red-haired and rowdy and lived with a black pimp who, she once declared, was the best lover she had ever known.

'How's that, then?' someone asked.

Polly squirmed inside her dress so that her breasts softly banged together. 'He licks me all over.'

It was an image which haunted Sergeant Mackintosh. 'I can just see that big, pink tongue,' he said. 'Like a bloody great labrador. In and out, round and round and old Polly going mad for it.'

He told the story each time that Polly appeared before the court but I had never heard him mention her purse. 'What's so special about it?' I enquired.

The sergeant pushed the envelope several inches further away from him. 'Let's hope you never find out.'

'Think about it,' said PC Croft. 'It's between her legs. That's where Polly keeps her readies.'

They all watched me expectantly. 'Perhaps you'd like

to wash your hands now,' said the sergeant, 'before you start touching our nice, clean charge sheets.'

Their teasing was not vindictive, but it was a relief when Eric announced that he had found us an office nearby. It was one room, midway up a flight of rickety stairs, sandwiched between a garment manufacturer's workshop and the Court Café where defendants sat nursing their cups of tea until it was time to surrender to their bail. Below us there was the constant chatter of crockery being washed or broken. Above us the ceiling vibrated with the hum of sewing machines. There was a grimy washbasin and a small window which looked out on a row of air-raid shelters, their hump backs gleaming in the rain. The lavatory was below stairs, adjacent to the kitchen. On my first visit I found a tray of jellies setting on the floor.

'We're a bit pushed for space,' explained Dave, who ran the café. He was both tall and fat, with a small moustache and a centre parting in his brilliantined hair. His movements were deft and finicky and in his white overall he sliced sandwiches and dissected shepherd's pie as if he was performing surgery. His face was impassive, a moon of suet occasionally streaked by sweat, but devoid of expression. He never deigned to wait on tables but stood behind his counter, flanked by two steaming urns, directing one harassed waitress and calling out orders which the customers themselves were expected to collect. Like ourselves he lived principally on the proceeds of crime – almost all his patrons visited him on their way to or from the court – but he chose to ignore the fact. His impartiality was priest-like. He did not serve; he ministered. I viewed him with respect, but I never ate his jellies.

Eric had lunch at the café every day. He used it as his boardroom and planned his strategy over cup after cup of tea in which, mysteriously, there floated globules of fat normally found in soup. Eric never noticed. His indifference to his surroundings was as impressive as Dave's. But he made no secret of his ambitions. Clearly, he said, the agency had to expand. There were courts in London where proceedings were going unreported, a state of affairs which distressed Eric both as a journalist and as a businessman.

We recruited additional staff. Eric's son, Ron – an actor whose talent for playing old men was enhanced by his premature baldness – joined us between engagements. I introduced Tony Linton, a pallid and lanky youth I had met in the hostel where I stayed before moving to the boarding house. And on two days each week Eric's daughter, Beryl, came in to attend to the book-keeping.

Cautiously, we extended our coverage to include Westminster County Court. But for me, said Eric, the time had come to develop North London. He made it sound like an extension of empire and as I caught the bus to Dalston Junction I felt as though I was embarking on a safari into unknown territory. Past Islington Green where Collins' Music Hall stood behind chocolate-brown pillars, the look of the houses changed. Rows of stunted terraces alternated with Georgian facades. There were gardens behind the houses and old fruit trees, heavy with blossom. A narrow stream disappeared beneath the road and on the bomb sites there were roses flowering above the willow-herb. I had a feeling that the country was not far away, as though a hundred years ago the builders who possessed the meadows had left behind them avenues into the past. The estates they had broken up had not been entirely obliterated. I saw quince and crab-apple and a pear climbing like a fountain towards the sun, but as we drove further east the gardens disappeared, the houses became stunted and the names on the shop-fronts were all foreign.

Mostly they were Jewish. The court itself stood opposite the Yiddish Theatre whose posters featured photographs of plump, middle-aged ladies appearing in plays remembered from pre-war Poland, or visiting cantors whose chants I could hear distantly through the stage-door during afternoon rehearsals. The theatre was already in decline. There was more drama, it seemed to me, in court where neighbourhood feuds involving as many as a dozen witnesses rumbled on for weeks at a time. There were passionate protests and accusations of calumny. Tufts of hair, torn out in a street brawl, were offered in evidence. One woman stripped off her dress to show a bite mark spanning her breast until the court matron, a zealous guardian of the proprieties, hauled it up again.

The magistrate was a benign and wily diplomat named Daniel Hopkin who listened to the endless wrangles and invariably ended the matter by binding over all parties to keep the peace. It was a formula which gave victory to no one. But the dispute had been aired, passions had been expressed; some sort of justice had been done.

Mr Hopkin seemed to me immensely wise. He had flowing white hair and rosy cheeks and his judgements were delivered in a lilting Welsh accent which could rise, if the occasion demanded it, to an Old Testament thunder. What impressed me was how skilfully he administered the law in a society which was fundamentally alien. The Jewish community was largely composed of *émigrés* or the children of *émigrés* from Europe. They were Ashkenazis; but there was an older generation of Sephardis, the aristocrats of the East End, who were entrenched in business and good works and whose sympathy could never be put at risk. There were also Greeks and Cypriots and Maltese, a growing number of West Indians and West Africans and to leaven the mixture, provincials from every part of the British Isles who had come to London for work or excitement and had frequently found neither.

Conveniently, the police believed that each race controlled its own branch of crime. The Jews, who were businessmen, ran the black market and were the principal receivers of stolen property. The Maltese and the West Indians were the most successful pimps and brothel keepers. Greeks and Cypriots, the chief caterers to North London, specialised in rationing offences. Housebreaking and crimes of violence were still basically British.

Sergeant Collins, the North London jailer, spelled out the litany to me on my first day at court. 'Don't think I'm prejudiced,' he added. 'I just happen to believe that a great deal of trouble in this country is going to be brought about by hairy-arsed niggers and it's as well to know in advance where it's coming from.' He was patently sincere and he was catholic in his discrimination. For Sergeant Collins 'nigger' meant anyone who was not born in the British Isles of Anglo-Saxon stock or whose accent indicated time spent north of Watford. Colour was not all that one had to watch out for. He was equally suspicious of the Scots and the Irish. 'Vicious bastards,' he said. 'Razors and bombs. That's what they're good with.'

He tried to be fair. He was courteous to prisoners. No one in his custody sustained an injury by accidentally falling down on their way from the cells. He did not solicit or accept bribes. In his spare time he helped to run a youth club. He was a humane and kindly man, but his view of the world was partial and pessimistic. He believed in being prepared and he saw it as his duty to prepare me too.

'What you've got to remember,' said Tim Mocock, the reporter from *The Hackney Gazette* who was to teach me the court routine, 'is that he's been let down a lot.'

'Who's let him down?'

Tim spread his arms to encompass the whole of Hackney. 'Lots of people. I've seen him give hand-outs to old drunks to go and get cleaned up and back they've come the next day. Pissed again.'

'I don't like his generalisations.'

'No one's asking you to. But they make sense.'

I was appalled by his cynicism. 'You don't believe all that stuff about hairy-arsed niggers?'

'Wait till you've been here a couple of months. See what you think then.'

'Not that,' I said virtuously.

Tim patted my shoulder. 'Good for you. We need someone round here to set an example.'

I had the sense to hold my tongue. Tim was perhaps ten years older than me, but a century shrewder. While holding on to the staff job which he despised, he free-lanced for several other papers. He wrote for trade journals, company magazines, anyone who would pay him, but – as Eric had indicated – his passion was for boxing. He looked like a fly-weight, short and pale, with slanting yellow eyes and jaw muscles which bulged like biceps beneath his cheek bones. He habitually wore double-breasted, pin-striped suits and shoes with sharply pointed toes. His hair was sandy and swept straight back as if it had been rinsed under a shower. He was already a tipster for several boxing columnists, but more than anything else he longed to see his own by-line in the American boxing magazine, *The Ring*. For Tim it was the ultimate ambition. Nothing else could match it.

Meanwhile, he believed in pursuing what was available. 'Always get the going rate,' he advised me the first day we met. 'If a solicitor asks you to take a note for him don't do him any favours. If the case is going to appeal he needs the magistrate's summing-up and you're the one with the shorthand. Give him what he wants but make sure you charge the full whack.'

'How much is that?'

'Three guineas a thousand words,' he said. 'I earned myself twenty quid last week.'

'That's more than I make in a month.'

'There you are then,' said Tim. 'Be in the right place at the right time and you're well away.'

For the next few weeks I worked under his supervision. He showed me how to compose a story; varying the style for different markets, opening with a quote whenever possible, checking the facts at all times. He also encouraged me to listen for the occasional joke from the bench. Usually they occurred during the most boring cases – a sign that the magistrate was reaching the end of his tether – and very rarely were they of any consequence. 'Never you mind,' said Tim. 'Keep your ears open. They're worth money.'

The Evening News, he explained, paid five shillings each for magisterial quips which they sprinkled through the news columns as light relief. Twenty or thirty fillers were used every day, which meant six or seven pounds for whoever supplied them. Together we examined the first edition and read alternate items aloud.

' "Perhaps the poor-box can underwrite the purchase of a razor blade.": West London magistrate to unshaven defendant.'

' "A silent woman is the perfect partner.": Thames Magistrate in matrimonial case.'

' "They say every dog must have his day. This isn't yours.": South London magistrate sentencing drunk to seven days imprisonment.'

I put the paper down. 'You're kidding,' I said. 'They don't pay five bob for those.'

'Scout's honour,' said Tim.

'I could make up better lines myself.'

He nodded wisely. 'So could we all. Some of us have done, now and again. But you've got to be careful. You can't make them too witty or they think there's a story they're missing. You can't have them too specific either. The case has to sound nice and vague. The other thing is, don't send them too many at a time. Just a nice little batch every week.'

We wrote the fillers on dull afternoons and most of them appeared in print. The evening papers regarded the stipendiary bench as a prime source of entertainment, and both *The Star* and *The Evening News* ran a daily column in which a minor case was treated as a human interest story with a wealth of Dickensian drollery. The *News* writer was named James A. Jones. He was stooped and bald and wore heavy, horn-rimmed glasses behind which he seemed anxious to hide. His modesty was unassumed and I would see him flinch when a magistrate – spotting him in the press box – would nod graciously and instantly begin to polish his metaphors.

'They just love to see themselves in the column,' said Mr Jones apologetically. 'They think they come across as such characters.'

There was no doubt that he was right. The sight of Mr Jones crouched over his pad noting down the picturesque details of some derelict, galvanized most magistrates into extraordinary action. Their warnings became ponderous, their asides waggish. Occasionally, they glanced in our direction as if expecting a prompt. When Mr Jones took his leave, bowing to the bench and sidling out through the jailer's door, their behaviour instantly reverted to normal.

'Don't worry about it,' said Tim, when I fretted over one outrageously ripe performance, 'nobody suffers.'

A good reporter, he argued, should be detached. We were there to observe, not to have opinions. He cared nothing for politics, unlike his *Gazette* colleague, Frank Maitland, who came from Scotland where he had formed a passionate attachment to the Independent Labour Party. His hero was the ILP founder, James Maxton. He had married the daughter of another ILP veteran and looked forward to the end of the war when, without question, he assured me the old gang would be swept away and the new society established. He had wiry black hair, a scrubby moustache and brilliant blue eyes. His suits were made of thick and hairy tweed which covered him like the pelt of an animal and his enthusiasm was so electric that every fibre seemed to stand on end as he denounced Tory councillors, turncoat MPs and press barons with equal fervour.

He rented a flat in Essex Road where George Orwell had once lived. 'Have you never read him?' he demanded. 'For God's sake, what are you doing with your mind? Give it some exercise. Put it to work.'

His wife, Pat, was a nurse; a gentle, hushing presence whose loyalties were identical to Frank's, but she expressed them with a quiet certainty that stayed in the mind longer than his rhetoric. She invited me home for a meal and as I sat at the kitchen table I looked out on to the lost gardens and broken walls of another century – a view which, until now, I had only glimpsed from the top deck of a passing bus – and I wondered whether they would survive the even greater changes that were on the way.

Coming to London in the middle of a war was like arriving late at a party and I felt it imperative, somehow, to catch up. So much had already happened in which I had taken no part. So much was going to happen but the chances were that I would be in the army and somewhere else when the great day came.

'How d'you like it with Eric?' asked Frank.

'It's all right.'

'It's the best training you could get,' he said. 'You should count your blessings.'

'There's not much money.'

'There's never much money. What d'you need it for?'

'Everything,' I said. 'Clothes mostly.'

'What kind of clothes?'

I owned one suit, a sports jacket, a pair of flannels and a pair of dark brown shoes. I had three ties, four shirts (two of them with Trubenized collars) and an overcoat which was already ragged at the cuffs. I needed an entire new wardrobe but what I coveted most was a trench-coat with epaulettes, a storm collar and a belt fringed with brass loops designed to carry grenades. The cheapest I had seen cost more than I could possibly afford, but I had already decided on a compromise. 'I could do with a riding mac,' I said. 'I've seen this one made of a rubberized material with straps inside it to go round your legs.'

'Are you taking up riding then?'

'Of course not. But it's a good buy.'

'How much?'

'Five pounds,' I said. 'If you lend me the money I'll pay you back.'

I had not meant to ask for the loan, but in some way the riding mac represented the future which, for me, had been indefinitely postponed. I felt justified in wanting a small part of it on account. The mac was my discovery. In the shop in Stoke Newington where I had seen it displayed a week earlier, it was waiting for me. The fit, I was certain, would be perfect. I was meant to be its owner. My desire was beyond logic; if I could not buy it I was quite prepared to steal it.

'All right,' said Frank. 'I'll lend you the money. We can't have you improperly dressed.'

I knew that he was amused, but he did not poke fun. Just as Tim was indifferent to politics, Frank cared nothing for clothes. But he sensed that he was investing in something more important than a raincoat. 'You shouldn't worry too much about the way things are,' he said. 'They'll get better. We're going to make them better.'

'I know.' I believed him in the way I believed the war would end and that truth would out, but the larger issues seemed so remote that they did not engage me. I heard them rumbling around me like wagons at night and the chances were, I supposed, that we would all converge unexpectedly at some point in the light of day. But not yet; not tomorrow or the next day. For the time being I could only follow my own path, taking one step at a time. 'Thanks for the money,' I said.

Frank waved me to the door. 'Go and buy your coat.'

'And come back and show it to us,' said Pat.

I got up early next morning and bought the coat on my way to work. Sergeant Collins inhaled its rubbery scent and inspected the straps which secured it to my legs. 'Going hunting?' he enquired.

It was not a comfortable garment to wear. The material was stiff and for the first few weeks it buckled rather than folded when I sat down. It was also noisy, booming like canvas in the wind when I walked at anything like my normal pace. There were ventilation holes in each armpit, but the fabric coaxed the sweat from my body and on mild days I was bathed in a constant dew of perspiration. None of it mattered. There was nothing modest about the riding mac but there was nothing apologetic either. Its swagger improved my morale. My self-confidence doubled. I began to answer policemen back.

'You know what I reckon,' said PC Croft, one day at Clerkenwell. 'He's gone and dipped his wick.'

There was, I realised, a military cut to the coat which gave me an undeserved glamour. But it was nothing compared to the uniform worn by Harry Barnes when he turned up at my digs one evening. Harry had been my friend at the Homes, an expert shoplifter and the envy of his contemporaries when he ran away to Blackpool with a girl from Darwen. After five days they were caught stealing milk from a doorstep but it had been worth it, he insisted. 'Non-stop shagging,' he told us when we asked what they had done and I remembered his expression, rapt and almost holy, as he uttered the words. He had soon quit the hostel in London where the Homes had found him a place and taken a job on the railways as a dining-car attendant. Once he had sent me £5, folded within a square of blue tissue paper so that no one would detect it. The last I had heard of him was that he was joining the army and the rumour turned out to be true. 'There's a soldier to see you,' announced Minnie as she set a helping of boiled cod in front of me.

Harry stood waiting in the hall, beret in hand. He watched Minnie trudge downstairs to the kitchen and wrinkled his nose. 'Fish for dinner? Smells bloody awful.'

'It's not bad.'

'Fancy something else?' He reached inside his tunic and showed me a wad of bank-notes. 'Come on. I'm loaded.'

It was embarkation pay, he told me, as we walked to the bus-stop. 'Mind you,' he said, 'they've had us lined up to go once before. I don't suppose it'll happen this time either.' I studied him out of the corner of one eye. His beret was plum-coloured and moulded his head so snugly that it seemed to have been glued into place. The toe-caps of his boots shone like liquorice. His trousers were sharply creased and hung neatly over the tops of his gaiters, and instead of a greatcoat he wore a blouse patterned with blotches of black, green and brown which reached to mid-thigh and ended in a tail flap pulled forward between his legs and fastened on either side with press studs as big as pennies.

'It's my jumping suit,' he said. 'The flap's supposed to keep my balls tucked away.'

Harry had been a paratrooper for six months. 'Everyone in my lot wanted to get into it. The pay's better for a start and you pull lots of tarts. They go for the uniform.' He rested one hand on the railings and struck a pose. He still had the face of a Red Indian, with flushed copper skin and a small beak of a nose. The beret and blouse gave him a rakish air as if, for him, the war was a party which he was going to enjoy. He flipped the collar of my riding mac with his forefinger. 'You look like an officer in that.'

'Sorry,' I said. 'I'll take it off if you like.'

'I'm not bothered. I've had officers for breakfast.'

I believed him. Once Harry had told me the secret of life: 'All you have to do is not care.' It was unlikely that he had changed his philosophy. 'D'you see anything of Sadie?' he asked.

'Quite a bit.'

'You mean you're still going strong?'

'She wants to get married.'

He raised his eyebrows and was slow to lower them. 'How about you?'

'I don't see why not.'

Harry hooted with laughter. 'You don't sound too keen. Tell me the important thing, though. Are you getting any?' When I hesitated he punched my shoulder, not hard but hard enough to push me off the kerb. 'Come on,' he said. 'Tell me how you're doing.'

I remembered how we had compared sexual notes when we were together at school, but the situation was different now. We were not sharing the same hunt. We had no common cause. I felt unaccountably wary. 'I'm doing all right,' I said.

'No better than that?'

'Well enough.'

'Why don't we give her a ring,' said Harry. 'I always liked old Sadie.'

I shook my head. 'Tonight's no good. She washes her hair on Tuesdays.'

'There's a war on,' said Harry. 'Didn't anybody tell you. I'm here on embarkation leave, wanting to see old friends and you say she won't come out because she's washing her hair.' He patted the bulge where he had stowed away his money. 'Let me talk to her. We'll have a few drinks and a nice little meal. My treat.' He pushed me towards a telephone box on the corner. You don't have to say anything. Just call her up and leave the rest to me.'

I could not think how to get out of it. I dialled the number at Sadie's digs and Harry instantly took the receiver from my hand. 'Hello,' he said, 'may I speak to Miss Bryant?' He told Sadie's landlady who he was and apologised for troubling her. He was polite and wheedling but when Sadie came on the line his manner changed abruptly. 'Tell me what clothes you've got on,' he said. 'That's right. I want to know what I'm taking out. Don't argue. Start from the top and go down.' He listened while Sadie recited her list, then groaned into the mouthpiece. 'That's enough. I'm in agony. Blue did you say? My favourite colour. And a suspender belt? I can't stand it.'

He covered the mouthpiece with his hand and winked at me. 'I've really got her going.'

'My turn,' I said, reaching for the phone.

'..... and when they've got no seams I draw a line on my legs with eyebrow pencil,' said Sadie.

'Fascinating,' I said.

'Who's that?'

'Who d'you think it is?'

'Oh, it's you,' said Sadie. She sounded less enthusiastic than she had been with Harry.

We agreed to meet at The Highbury Barn Tavern in half an hour's time. 'Tell her the saloon bar,' said Harry. 'We're not slumming tonight.' He would not let us pay for anything. I drank bitter, he drank rum and Sadie drank gin and orange. Harry kept ordering more drinks. He started to take off his blouse, then changed his mind when he had unbuttoned the tail flap and for an hour or more stood with it dangling behind him like the seat in an old-fashioned pair of combinations.

I remembered Frank's remark the night he lent me the money to buy the riding mac. 'Improperly dressed,' I said and burst out laughing.

'Better undressed,' said Harry. 'A far, far better thing.'

It was dusk when we left the pub, walking three abreast with Sadie between us. Both Harry and I had arms around her waist. She swayed from side to side, tugging in opposite directions. 'You'll have me over,' she said.

'Never,' said Harry, grabbing her more tightly. His hand slid down until it covered one of her buttocks and Sadie jerked her haunches like a horse trying to dislodge a fly.

I pretended not to notice, but I could see Harry's fingers denting the gabardine of her coat. 'Hands off,' I said at last.

'What?' He took two steps forward and two steps back as if struggling to keep his balance. 'What's the matter?'

'Leave her alone.'

He was suddenly sober. His index finger jabbed me in the chest and I winced with pain. 'Don't tell me what to do,' said Harry. 'There's enough people think they can do that. Why don't you ask her what she wants. You might get a shock.'

He leaned forward, his head thrust towards me as if he was straining against a leash and I was reminded of a terrier that lived three doors down from us in the avenue at home. One of the fence palings was loose and the dog waited behind it until someone walked by. Then it would thrust its head through the gap, snapping and snarling, but unable to make contact because of the palings that held it on either side. The dog knew that it would never bite anyone and so did we. But it was still a frightening experience. Harry had the same effect. I swallowed hard and tried to keep my voice level. 'I'm asking you to keep your hands off.'

'Asking or telling?'

'Asking,' I said.

He nodded gravely as if that had been the issue all along. 'That's different. I don't mind being asked.' He allowed himself to be drunk once more, snapping to attention so that his boots chimed on the pavement, saluting first Sadie then me before linking arms and marching us across the road and into the café.

I had no appetite but I drank a glass of red wine while Harry disappeared into the kitchen to talk to the waiter. 'All fixed,' he said when he came out and fifteen minutes later we were served with steak and chips, a meal which did not appear on the menu.

Rationing was still severe, but money could usually find a way round the restrictions. 'At our camp they chuck away tons of food every day,' said Harry. 'Meat, bread, potatoes, you name it. Most of it goes for pig swill.'

Sadie chewed on a morsel of steak. 'Disgusting.'

'You're paying for it,' said Harry. 'It's all tax-payers' money.' He emptied a tumbler of wine. 'I don't give a toss. I won't be there after next week.'

'Where d'you think they'll be sending you?'

'Where d'you suppose?' Harry put his fingers to the corners of his eyes and pushed them upwards. With his coppery skin and slicked-back hair he looked instantly Japanese.

'I don't fancy that,' I said.

Harry smiled understandingly. 'Don't worry, son. We'll have it sorted out by the time you get there.'

The sirens sounded as we left the café and Sadie held my arm tightly. Any reminder of the war made her clutch people and objects as if she was fearful that they might be wrenched away. She was not passionate by nature, but she was excited by melodrama. Her mouth grew hot, her body became heavy. It was when she made love best.

There was no opportunity that night. Harry was staying at a services hostel at Waterloo, but he insisted on walking back with us. 'Don't mind me,' he said as we hovered on the doorstep and he turned his back as Sadie and I fell into each other's arms. The effects of the night's drinking had worn off, but we were both giddy with a lust which was sharpened by Harry's silent presence. I pressed Sadie against the wall and she seemed to spread beneath me like butter. Her dress puckered under my hand and then our mouths slid apart as she peered over my shoulder. 'Not now,' she whispered, 'not while he's here.'

I let her go and she leaned back, gasping for breath. Harry joined us. 'Can I kiss you goodbye?' he enquired formally and when Sadie nodded he pulled her towards him and covered her face with his own. It was like seeing an animal feed. There was a full moon which made Sadie's skin shine like paper, but it was blotted out by Harry's head as he made his meal.

It went on for a long time. I wanted to pull them apart, but I hesitated. Harry had asked permission to say goodbye and Sadie had given it. For her he represented the real war; the one which we had so far escaped. We had heard the sirens. Somewhere that night people would die. It could not be wrong to acknowledge our survival and our luck.

Miles to the east a bomb went off and Harry raised his head. I almost expected him to lick his chops like a great, satisfied cat, but instead he merely corrected the angle of his beret and shrugged his blouse into a tighter fit across his shoulders. 'I'll drop you a line,' he told Sadie.

She nodded weakly. 'If you like.'

'See you tomorrow,' I said.

She nodded again and fitted the key into the lock. Her lips and her face were puffy, as though she had been crying. She did not want to look at me and hurried into the dark hall-way. We were all hiding something, I thought. But it was difficult to put a name to and for each of us it was different.

I walked with Harry to the main road and saw him on to a bus. If he was not posted abroad, he said, he would let me know. We should keep in touch. When the bus drove away he hung from the platform and waved until it turned the corner. 'Abyssinia,' he shouted. 'Don't let the bastards grind you.'

I remembered the words. He had written them as a postscript to the letter in which he sent me five pounds soon after he had left the Homes. We had all changed since then, I decided. Our deceits were proof that we were growing up.

Three

I WENT TO SEE Emma at the house where she was working near Guildford. Her employers were an army colonel and his wife and their front hall was hung with regimental photographs. I studied the faces, barred with moustaches and browned by an Indian sun, and felt the usual prickle of unease that authority always produced in me.

'They're not like that,' said Emma. 'They're very kind. They've lent me a cot and given me a complete layette. I've been very lucky.'

She was much fatter than when we had last met. I put my hand on her stomach, half-expecting to feel the kick of the baby it contained. But nothing stirred. 'It's at night she moves about,' said Emma. 'Twice round the houses before supper-time.'

'How do you feel?'

'I feel marvellous. Never better. The doctors say I was made to have babies.'

She had booked in at the local hospital and was attending ante-natal clinics twice a week. The baby was expected in early spring. There were still several months to go but she had already made plans. 'I know it's early days,' she said, 'but I know what I'm going to do. There's a crying need for teachers and I've always been good with children. If you're prepared to go where you're needed there's very often a house that goes with the job. That's what I'm after.'

'I expect you'll get it then.'

She looked at me quizzically. 'Why d'you say that?'

'I've never seen anyone so determined.'

'Just as well isn't it.' She buttered bread and cut it into thin slices. 'Mind you, I've got to get through a teacher's training course first.'

'Have you applied?'

'And been accepted. I'll be the oldest in my class.'

'You're not old,' I said.

'Thirty-one this year.'

Emma was no longer twice my age as she had been when we first made love and the difference between us, I realised, would signify less the older we grew. But there was still a gap of fifteen years which could be measured in assurance as well as time. I imagined a packet from the chemist, dapper in waxed paper, with a label which stated unequivocally by how much I fell short.

'Time marches on,' I said. 'I'll be in the army soon.'

'It'll be a while yet,' said Emma. 'A lot can happen before then.'

I knew she was right but it was irritating to be told, however gently, that I was making a fuss. 'It's difficult to plan ahead,' I complained.

'I know something about that.'

'I know you do, but this is different. I don't know where I should concentrate. I'm learning a lot with Eric. But what happens next?'

'Wait and see,' said Emma. 'Enjoy the time that's been given to you. Don't try to use it up in advance.'

We were sitting at the kitchen table. There was a plate of potted-meat sandwiches, strawberry jam and a small dish of clotted cream. I remembered how she used to make it when we were at the Homes, leaving a bowl of milk in the oven overnight and skimming off the cream in the morning. She intercepted my glance as I watched her cut a crust in two and pop one half into her mouth. 'I'm eating for two now,' she said.

After tea we went for a walk. It was a cold, dry day and the bare tips of the trees which fringed the playing fields on the opposite side of the road seemed to scratch the sky. I told Emma about my digs and how I sat by the window, notebook in my lap, watching the pigeons jockey for position in the treetops below.

'Are you writing any poetry?' asked Emma.

'Not much.'

The truth was that I was writing none at all. At school it had been easier. There had been acceptable subjects, with Nature the hot favourite, and I had rather enjoyed the reputation of being the moody observer of the passing scene. For a while I had accepted commissions to compose verses for boys in my class to inscribe in the extravagant, hand-painted birthday cards which were considered the mark of true love by their girl-friends. But the sentiments I expressed were less colourful than the roses and garlands pictured by the artist. Business fell off and I was not surprised.

'It's not that you write bad rhymes,' explained one of my patrons. 'But when you've paid half a dollar for a card you want something just as fancy to put inside it.'

Now I had no patrons and nothing to write about. I felt sometimes as though I was an enormous sponge absorbing the residue of sights and sensations as they rinsed through me. The object was to hang on to as much as possible, cramming the honeycomb to feed me in times to come. When I read of an old man found dead in his flat with every room filled from floor to ceiling with piles of newspapers I experienced a surge of fellow feeling. The papers went back forty years; the flat contained spinneys of newsprint, gallons of ink. The old man may have been eccentric but I understood his desire to hoard the trivia of time, banking it in the hope that one day a pattern would emerge which would explain his life and purpose. I longed for a similar moment of revelation. My notebooks filled up with notes, but they did not speak to me.

'What does your mother think of your job?' asked Emma.

'She's glad I've found something to do.'

When I had written to tell her I was joining a Court Reporting Service I had not explained that the business of the agency was crime rather than the affairs of State. She was at first confused and then angry. 'How should I be expected to know what you meant?' she demanded when I went to see her several weeks later.

'I'd have thought it was common sense.'

'Don't you common sense me,' she said. 'Your Uncle Percy didn't understand either.'

'I'm not surprised.'

'What do you mean by that?' It was unwise to make fun of any of my relations but I found it hard to resist taking the occasional pot-shot. It was my Uncle Percy who had escorted me to the Homes that snowy day in February and I knew that he still blamed me for the inhospitality of the governor who had not offered him a bed for the night.

'You think alike,' I said. 'If you find something obscure, so does he. It's a family characteristic.'

My mother sniffed. 'It's a pity you don't have more of them.'

'We can't all be perfect.'

'We can try.'

Soon after she had known that she was pregnant, Emma had visited my mother. Partly, I assumed, it was to see how she might react to the prospect of becoming a grandmother, but chiefly it was to reassure her that I was behaving sensibly in looking for work in London. The meeting had not been a success. My mother knew nothing of the relationship between Emma and me, but it was clear where Emma's sympathies lay. I was not condemned out of hand for my refusal to return home. I was not going to London for entirely selfish reasons. I was not called disloyal.

My mother felt that an ally had let her down. As a former headmistress she had a reverence for authority and she was disconcerted when Emma, who she had supposed was on the same side, questioned her most basic assumptions. 'I'm sure she's good at her job,' she allowed, when we eventually discussed the visit, 'but she's got some queer ideas. It wasn't like that in my day.'

'Nothing's like it was in your day.'

'More's the pity.'

Emma was painfully aware that the encounter had gone amiss. 'All I was trying to do was make peace,' she said. 'You shouldn't be at each other's throats all the time.'

It was not going to be like that with our baby she declared. She was going to find work and make a home where they would be together. She did not ask for my help. I was travelling in other directions. 'But you must keep in touch,' she said. 'Promise me that.'

'Of course I will.'

'And don't go and do anything silly.'

'I don't know what you mean.'

'Oh yes you do,' said Emma. 'You've made a good start, but you've got a long way to go. Don't slow yourself down.'

The warning was delivered softly, but I recognised it for what it was. Since the night out with Harry my feelings for Sadie had become confused. I could see and even detail the differences between us, but at the same time the attraction had grown stronger. When her pale face had been blotted out by Harry's head I had wanted her so fiercely that, even remembering the moment of eclipse, I felt giddy. Knowing that she was wanted by someone else made her more desirable. I was tormented by the thought of competition. It was like wearing rough wool next to the skin. My circulation raced, but the itch was unbearable. I longed simultaneously for the instant relief of sex and the long, uneventful peace which I imagined marriage to be. I persuaded myself that I was in love.

We tried to domesticate our relationship. On Saturday nights we went dancing at Holborn Hall. There was a seven-piece band, wrapped like cigars in shiny grey suits, with a girl singer who slightly resembled Marian Hutton, the vocalist in the Glenn Miller film, *Orchestra Wives*. She featured all the songs from the film and as the band played *At Last* the spotlight seized her, the saxophones sighed and Sadie and I clung together in the hot dusk while the glitter ball revolved above us, splashing our faces with silver until the house lights came up again and the spell was broken.

There was always a sprinkling of American servicemen who staked out their own corner of the hall where they jived fervently to *The Jersey Bounce* and *Pennsylvania Six Five Thousand*. Their look of dedication never altered even when sweat plated their faces, and they chewed gum incessantly as though it contained a secret ingredient, a drug perhaps, which was the source of their boundless energy.

The most dedicated dancers brought their own partners; tense, rubbery girls who trucked and spun through intricate routines without missing a beat or conceding that any other couple shared the floor. They were exclusive. No one else dared ask them to dance. Between sets they sat together, comparing bracelets and puffing sulkily on filter-tipped cigarettes. They always appeared to be in a bad temper. When they were not dancing they were bored. Their make-up was thick and even, with rims of blue around the eyes and mulberry mouths which ignored the outline of the lips beneath. Collectively they were known as 'Yank bait'.

Not all the Yanks had girls. One Saturday a tall lieutenant in pink trousers and olive green tunic asked Sadie to dance. 'But I don't know your style,' she said.

'Sure you do.'

She made a token gesture towards me. 'I'm with my friend.'

'You don't mind do you, sir?'

I felt the usual pile-up of emotions, but managed to smile grudgingly. 'Not if she doesn't.'

'All right then,' said Sadie. She rose from her chair and took his hand. 'Nothing fancy, mind.'

The band was playing *In the Mood*. It was everyone's favourite and the floor was crowded. Chalk dust quivered in the air. There was a smell of scent and sweat and cigarette smoke as complicated and familiar as my own breath. Sadie and the lieutenant disappeared into the crowd but I caught sight of them again in the far corner. The lieutenant held Sadie at arm's length, guiding her with the tips of his fingers while she jerked and twisted in the centre of an admiring crowd. Her skirt rode up over her thighs. Her breasts jogged busily beneath her sweater. Her face had set like custard in a look of disdain as if she preferred not to know what her body was doing. The tune throbbed through its two false endings then soared into its blithe finale. The lieutenant led Sadie back across the floor and seated her at our table. 'Much obliged,' he said and tore off a small salute.

I smiled grudgingly. 'That's OK.'

'She's a great dancer,' he said. 'We were really going there.'

'I could see that.'

'Maybe we could do it again.'

'Sorry,' I said. 'Not tonight. We have to leave in a minute. Another time perhaps.'

'Sure thing.' He nodded to Sadie and marched briskly away.

She waited until he was out of earshot, then leaned across the table. 'Who said we were leaving?'

'I thought you were ready.'

'You could try asking.'

'All right,' I said. 'Are you ready to go?'

She folded her arms and sat heavily back in her chair as if she had just dropped anchor. 'No, I'm not.'

'How long do you want to stay?'

'I've not decided yet. I'll let you know.'

For another hour we sat and watched the dancers. There were quicksteps and foxtrots and sambas. There was a contest in which the couples who moved when the music stopped were eliminated. There was a ladies' excuse me and a Paul Jones. There was a conga in which several people kicked off their shoes and finally there was the last waltz.

'Come on,' I said. 'I'm sorry if I upset you.'

She felt soft and slack in my arms as though the flesh of her body had turned to liquid which shifted its weight as we danced so that, whatever the motion, not a drop was spilled. I smelled the shampoo in her hair and as the lights dimmed I tilted her face and kissed her. 'I

love you,' I said, surprising myself by how sincerely I
meant it.

'I love you,' said Sadie, her eyes brimming with unshed
tears.

Our alliance regained the weight it had lost, although
at times we both seemed to be willing it to work in
a way which it had once done without effort. Instinc-
tively, we tried to save it from strain by doing ordinary
things. Every other week we treated ourselves to a meal
at the Salad Bowl in Coventry Street where for one and
sixpence you could load your plate from the buffet and
come back for second or third helpings at no extra charge.
On Sunday mornings we took long walks through the
empty streets of the City, pausing by bomb sites to stare
through the charred sockets of windows and trace the
configuration of vanished offices by the veining of flues
and the bleached and bold patterns of wallpaper, stamped
by lost filing cabinets and calendars turned to tinder.
In the afternoons we went to Hyde Park Corner to listen
to the speakers. Donald Soper drew the biggest crowd.
He was one of my mother's favourites on the wireless
and I was able to report how he routed the hecklers
who surrounded his soap-box, engaging them in Chris-
tian cross-talk and saving the punch line for himself.

There was also a Communist who, like Frank Maitland,
looked forward to the end of the war. But his forecast
was less optimistic. 'Russia's our ally now,' he would
say, 'but just you wait and see what happens when we
no longer need her help. The West will turn on the Soviet
Union and the back-slapping will turn to back-stabbing.
You may laugh, comrades. But remember what I say now.'
He was a swarthy, twinkling man whose warnings were
delivered with irony as well as passion.

'Do you believe him?' I asked Sadie.

'Don't ask me. I don't know about politics.'

'Don't you care?'

'What's the point of caring. There's nothing we can
do about it.'

'Of course there is. Why d'you think we have elections?'

'There won't be an election for ages.'

'Sooner than you think,' I said importantly.

'What do you know about it?'

'More than you. That's obvious.' I knew nothing except what Frank had told me and what I absorbed at Speakers' Corner but, without the burden of facts, I could sense an impending upheaval as though a dragon dozing in its den had stirred beneath us. 'There's got to be a change,' I said. 'It's how the system works. Things can't stay as they are.'

Sadie put her arm through mine. 'I know that much.'

'And we've got to be ready,' I said. It was comforting to utter truisms which no one needed to contradict. They put an end to argument and at the same time made me feel that the conversation had been of some value.

Our problem, always, was how to end the day. We had devised a routine which was uneventful but intimate, but what it lacked was some physical pledge which assured us that we belonged to each other. Making love in the front porch was not only uncomfortable but unsatisfying. I dreamed constantly of lying down with Sadie in a bed, whose sheets smelled of lavender and whose springs tipped us irresistibly into each other's arms. It was the situation that attracted me even more than the sexual possibilities. What I longed for was a private place where we could be at ease and the more I thought of it the more unjust it seemed that we should be denied such a simple need.

The memory of Minnie and Lily's assault on the female who had dared to set foot in the house was still vivid, but as I walked Sadie home, tumescent and desperate, I could think of no alternative. One rainy night we decided to take a chance. For over an hour we loitered under dripping trees until every window in the house was dark. It was past one o'clock but from the factory across Highbury Fields where electrical parts were assembled came the steady champ of presses. The late shift was at work, but no one else was awake. We slipped into the hall and inhaled the essence of the house, a mixture of dust and polish and cooking, and stealthily I put my hand in the small of Sadie's back and propelled her up the stairs.

There were some which creaked under pressure and one which actually screamed like an animal in pain. I steered her safely to my room and closed the door behind us. With infinite care I pulled the bed into the centre of the room. The walls were thin and I sometimes woke to hear Barrett the librarian snoring only inches away. He claimed that he was a heavy sleeper, but I was not prepared to take his word for it.

We undressed quickly and climbed into the narrow bed. The sheets were icy and for several minutes we lay clutching each other, afraid to stir. The cold was savage and any movement threatened to extinguish the core of heat that lay between us. Gradually I felt my toes thaw, then my chest, my arms and my thighs. Sadie's breath was hot in the furrow of my shoulder, but when she breathed in the warmth was replaced by the chilly prickle of condensation.

I whispered directly into her ear: 'All right now?'

She nodded and stroked my back. Her touch was light, signalling nothing but affection, but I felt myself stir and thicken. It was the first time we had been in a bed together and I wanted my reaction to be different. I rolled to one side so that the iron frame dug into my spine, but it would have been more effective if it had lain between us.

'What's wrong?' Sadie hissed.

I guided her hand downwards. 'I just wanted us to lie here for a while, but this happens.'

'We don't have to do anything about it.'

She was right, I thought. But my longing for naked but chaste companionship (which would have proved, however briefly, that our bonding was not dependent on sex) was quickly being replaced by a lust which lit the inside of my head like a magnesium flare. The white

light and the heat which now consumed us were one
and the same. I gave up trying to think and let myself
burn.

When my head cleared I was lying with Sadie beneath
me, clutching the bed frame with both hands as if it
was a raft bearing us over dangerous seas. It had been
important, I recalled, to hold on. But as the house settled
down and the fire and water subsided I was appalled
by my lack of control. I had taken no precautions and
confessed as much.

'Don't worry,' said Sadie. 'It's my safe period.'

I offered a silent prayer and slid over on to my side.
It was still dark but I could see rifts in the cloud and
the first birds were already piping among the wet leaves.
'Half an hour and we'll have to move,' I said.

We dressed without putting on the light and crept
down the stairs as carefully as we had climbed up them.
I closed the front door with a click that even I could
barely hear and, hand in hand, we walked the half mile
to Sadie's digs. The pavement was the colour of iron,
but by the time we reached the house the sun had risen
turning the flagstones to pale gold.

I framed Sadie's face between my finger and thumb.
'Are you happy?'

'Tired.'

'Go to bed. You've got a couple of hours.'

We leaned against each other like exhausted runners
fondly reliving the race, then Sadie pushed me away.
'Go on,' she said, 'go home.'

That afternoon I fell asleep in court. I had been trying
to follow a long and complicated case of dangerous driving which involved a taxi and a private car. Anything
which concerned a taxi-driver meant hours of evidence
and cross-examination because a clean licence and frequently a job was at stake and a full report was always
wanted by *The Green Badge Journal*. I stayed alert throughout the case for the prosecution and was bracing myself
for the defence when my eyelids fell like blinds and refused to rise. I tried to resist the delicious languor that

possessed me, but failed. I awoke to feel PC Croft's finger prodding me in the ribs and the entire court staring in my direction.

The magistrate peered over his glasses. 'Are we disturbing you?'

'What? I'm sorry.'

'You were snoring,' hissed PC Croft.

For several seconds I could barely take in what he was saying, but suddenly I was aware of what I had done. I bowed to the bench. 'I'm very sorry, sir.'

'And may we proceed?'

'Certainly, sir.' I sat down, my cheeks burning. Sleeping in court was not unknown. Even magistrates had been observed to doze through testimony which would eventually be weighed by a higher court. But I had made an exhibition of myself and it would not be forgotten.

Eric had already heard about it by the time I got back to the office. 'You're not ill?' he asked suspiciously.

'Just a bit weary.'

'You can't burn the candle at both ends, you know.'

'I know that. I've not been sleeping too well.'

'We all need eight hours,' declared Eric. 'If you're still growing you probably need more. You can't do your work properly otherwise.'

I showed him my notebook. 'Don't worry about the story. I've got it all down.'

'You're sure?'

'Positive.' My notes included three pages gleaned from the clerk of the court, but I chose not to mention that.

'We don't want word getting round that we're inefficient. And you know what I've said about accuracy. It's vital in this business.'

I was tired of apologising for my brief snooze, but I understood the reasons for Eric's anxiety. Not only did he live in constant dread of a writ for libel; he also worried about me. When I came to know him better I realised that he worried for the world. I was well to the bottom of his list of causes which ranged from war refugees to the grass-cutting rota at the Friends' Meeting House, but I had my place in the roster. My training as a reporter was synonymous with my moral welfare and Eric held himself responsible.

It was a burden which made him susceptible to a variety of appeals, most of them cynical, and his anguish in trying to determine whether a demand was justified, inspired a performance which was best judged in terms of pure drama. Money was the topic which produced the keenest reaction. Calculating the linage of a story which appeared in half a dozen papers and which might earn him several pounds, Eric would squirm in his chair as if the seat had been wired to the mains. Sometimes he would hum loudly and out of tune, or pluck at his hair until it stood on end like a dunce's cap. If someone asked him for a rise the shock would bring him to his feet where he stood coiling one leg round the other, scratching dispiritedly at armpit and crotch until the moment of decision had been reached.

He made skilful use of props, especially his spectacles which were polished to a rare brilliance while he debated whether or not to hire part-time help, or chewed until the arms looked like a puppy's plaything, while time off was negotiated. He was not mean, but deeply distrustful of his own generosity. Flag-sellers and fund-raisers saw Eric as a soft touch. He found it easier to give than to receive but there were times when, without warning, he would refuse a donation or deny a request, after which he would fall silent as though he needed rest and quiet in which to repair the violence done to his system.

As Christmas approached, so did the arrangements for time off. Most cases which came to court during the peak days of the holiday were instantly remanded and the papers which did appear had less room for news of petty crime. But full coverage, said Eric, was still essential. 'It's a legal requirement,' he explained. 'When a paper's published a report of a man being charged, and fails to give equal space if he's acquitted, we've broken the law.'

It was a fear which he transmitted like flu. For hours

we endured argument and rebuttal to secure the vital paragraph which it was our obligation to provide. There were cases which I sometimes believed would never end. A scrap-dealer charged with receiving stolen lead made six separate appearances before being found not guilty. An assault case in which the defendant was an Arab who spoke no known dialect was adjourned again and again until an interpreter could be found. Any prosecution in which a Government department was involved was destined to unfold at a snail's pace over an obstacle course of regulations and sub-sections and amendments until the magistrate delivered his ritual observations on red tape and, with a matching sense of tradition, our report would be published under the heading 'Magistrate Slams Ministry'.

Christmas made no difference to the pattern of the programme, but covering it as we were supposed to do became more of a chore. There was a steady build-up of the holiday spirit. The jailer's office at North London was hung with paper chains. The warrant office, which supervised the service of summonses and the collection of fines, smelled like a delicatessen with the assortment of cheeses and hams, shrouded in foil or trussed with string, which local traders slid hopefully over the counter. 'Don't think of them as bribes,' advised the warrant officer. 'Think of them as tributes to our understanding.' His name was Battersby. He had been a sergeant for fifteen years and still remembered the disastrous police strike of the 1920s. All it had taught him, he said, was to look after number one. 'No one else will,' he assured me. 'Just you bear it in mind.'

Although he disapproved on principle, Eric also paid his Christmas levy to the police. Sergeants were given a box of fifty cigarettes; constables, a packet of twenty. 'It's all wrong,' he complained. 'But, you know, I think they expect it.'

Tradition also required him to pay a Christmas bonus to Tony Linton and myself. We tried to guess how much it would be, but it was not easy to anticipate what the previous month's earnings would amount to, or how much Eric would be subscribing to the flock of charities which rattled their collecting boxes with fresh vigour as the season accelerated. Eric's solvency was always delicately poised between his income and his outgoings. He had no reserves. A plus or minus could tip the scales either way and it was unwise to look too far ahead.

I was counting both on a bonus and at least three days off to visit my mother. But I was in a dilemma. Sadie had moved into new digs, following an argument with the widow who had objected to her coming home in the small hours. She now lived in a large semi-detached house in Aberdeen Park with a married couple named Carrington. He was a retired builder, rosy cheeked and corpulent, with a gaunt, harried wife who endlessly mourned their daughter, an only child, who had died the previous year.

Sadie had taken her place. No one had meant it to happen. The Carringtons had advertised a bed-sitting room, hoping for company. 'But when I opened the door and saw her standing there I was speechless,' Mrs Carrington told me. 'She's the image of our Dodie. Different coloured hair and half an inch taller. But they could have been sisters; the same age, the same way with them. Like as peas from the same pod.'

I learned how Dodie had been killed in a road accident. The car which knocked her down had failed to stop and she had died without regaining consciousness. The Carringtons kept her room as it had been when she was alive. On her first tour of the house Sadie remarked on the vases of fresh flowers, upstairs and down. There were freesias in a bowl on a bedside table. 'My favourites,' she said, and Mrs Carrington had taken it as an omen.

'They were Dodie's favourites too,' she said, and Sadie moved in the next day.

The intensity of the welcome was more than she had bargained for. She was not treated as a lodger, but as a member of the family. The rent which the Carringtons had stipulated in their advertisement was halved. On her first night she found a hot-water bottle in her bed and each morning she was awakened with a cup of tea brought by Mr Carrington. 'It was the only way we could get our Dodie to work on time,' he explained. She was urged to bring her friends home and I was issued with a standing invitation to Sunday lunch. Partly, I suspected, it gave the Carringtons an opportunity to look me over and I became aware of a fond surveillance which was not only embarrassing, but inconvenient.

No curfew was imposed. Promptly at ten o'clock the Carringtons went to bed, leaving us the sitting room with its electric fire and ample settee. But above us the floor boards creaked. There were surreptitious night noises and we leapt apart at each rustle and twang. We never felt entirely alone or comfortable together. The Carringtons were either with us or in the next room or over our heads. We could not complain; it was their house and we had accepted their hospitality. But in return we gave something of ourselves. No actual demand was ever made, but we were in no doubt that it was expected of us.

'We're going to have a lovely Christmas,' announced Mrs Carrington over the roast beef one Sunday (Mr Carrington had an understanding with the butcher which made nonsense of the ration) and Sadie and I knew that our presence was taken for granted.

I did not mind spending Christmas with the Carringtons. They were kind people and generous hosts. But my mother expected me to spend the holiday with her. It was not a prospect I looked forward to with any pleasure. My mother so bitterly resented my being in London that whether I went home for a weekend or a fortnight it was never long enough. She would measure my brief stay against the months that she spent alone and inevitably find proof of my not caring. Her own childhood became the ideal with which she punished us both. 'I can remember it like yesterday,' she would say. 'We were so happy. All of us together. None of us wanted to leave.'

'Nor did I,' I was driven to point out. 'It was you who sent me away. I didn't choose to go.'

'There was nothing else I could do.'

'I know that. I'm not blaming you. But stop blaming me.'

'You could live at home now. There's nothing to stop you.'

'I work in London.'

'That's nothing to do with it. You could work here. But, oh no, it's those smart London friends of yours. You'd rather be with them than me.'

I thought of Eric and the office vibrating with the sewing machines and PC Croft with his morning assembly of drunks and derelicts, and the contrast between the actuality and what my mother imagined made me smile.

It was like rubbing salt on the wound. 'There's nothing to laugh at Mister Cleverdick! Just think of me sometimes when you're out enjoying yourself and imagine how you'd like it!'

We repeated the same argument again and again and although I tried to divert her it was like hearing a part-song in which, once the first bars had been sung, it was impossible not to take the second line. The only sure way of avoiding the quarrel was to stay away. But I knew I could not do that and the thought of Christmas filled me with apprehension.

'Can't you tell her you're working,' said Sadie.

'She'd never believe me.'

'What if it was true?'

'But it's not,' I said miserably. It was one thing to deny my mother information; telling her about Emma would have helped no one. But it was quite another matter to tell her lies which she would, inevitably, detect. I wished that there was somewhere to go – away from Sadie, away from my mother – where there was no guilt and no reproaches. I longed to be invisible or at least anonymous. Suddenly I could see the advantages in being called-up. In the army I would have to obey orders, but they would be given impartially. I would not be singled out for special duties. I could hide myself in the ranks.

The agency afforded no such cover. The Friday before Christmas I was given an extra week's pay as my bonus and four days off. I caught the train to Stoke after finishing work on the twenty-second and spent the entire journey rehearsing what I had to say. It was a waste of time. My announcement was received with incredulity.

'I'm sorry,' I said. 'I have to go back on Christmas Eve.'

I had sounded warning notes in my letters over the previous two weeks, but my mother had ignored them.

'You have to do what?'

'Go back,' I said. 'I've promised to spend Christmas Day with friends. We'll have two whole days and I'll be back next month for my birthday.' I realised that I was talking far too quickly, reeling off my excuses with an assumed jauntiness that sounded more and more bogus with every word.

'Why bother?'

'What do you mean?'

'Why bother to come home for your birthday? Why bother to come home at all? You don't care about me. You don't care about the family. You're completely selfish.'

'I'm sorry,' I said again.

'I suppose it's that girl you're going to.'

I shook my head. 'It's not just her. If I stay here we'll quarrel like we always do. I'm tired of it.'

'What have you got to be tired of!' My mother was sitting in a cane armchair which squeaked each time that she moved as though mice were trapped in the binding. She held herself very straight and her cheeks were flushed. She was too angry to cry and I was glad of it. 'I'm the one who's tired of being cooped up in these four walls, day in, day out. Change places with me and see how you feel.'

'I know how you feel,' I said.

'Rubbish!' She stood up, brushing aside the arm I put out to support her and violently jerked open the door of the sideboard. She reached inside and scooped out two small parcels wrapped in Christmas paper. She did not pick them up but swept them on the floor at my feet. 'Those are your presents,' she said. 'I'm sure they're not as grand as anything you'll be getting from your smart friends. But you might as well have them.'

I picked them up and put them on the table. 'I'm not opening them now. I'll save them for later.'

'Why save them? It won't be any different twenty-four hours from now. You'll still be going back. And I'll still be here.'

'You're making a fuss about one day,' I said.

'Christmas Day!'

'There's nothing special about it.'

'You've made sure of that.' The tears were coming now and I wished desperately that everything I had said could be unsaid. I felt sick and ashamed but, at the same time, I knew that we had reached a turning point. Perhaps we had even passed it. I had been as bad as she had always supposed I could be. I had been cruel and thoughtless and whatever I did in the future to redeem myself, the crime had been committed. It was on my record, built into my bones.

We were polite to each other for the next two days. At lunchtime on Christmas Eve we opened our presents. My mother had given me a diary and a pen and pencil set and I gave her lavender-water and talc. We listened to a carol service on the wireless and we had mince-pies for tea. Then I brought my case downstairs and left it by the front door. 'I should be off,' I said. 'The train's at seven.'

'What time will you get to London?'

'Around ten.'

'Not too late. That's good.'

'I'll be back for my birthday. A weekend if I can manage it.'

She gave me her bravest smile; the one which, as a

child, I had always remembered as an illustration from a song sheet. The tears were imminent, but held in check. The chin was firm; the mouth tremulous. There was something misty about the expression, like weather which was soon to change. 'Only a month to go,' she said. 'I'll look forward to that.'

Mary came down the steps with me to the front gate. 'You've done it this time, my lad.'

'I know.'

'Is that all you can say?'

'I can't help it.'

She gave me a hard look and shrugged her shoulders. 'More's the pity. You'd best be off then.'

She did not kiss me goodbye and I did not look back. I managed to find a corner seat on the train and stared at the blackout blind all the way to London, as though behind it my reflection lay in wait, ready to surprise me with a face that was stamped with evidence of my new callousness.

I hurried round to Sadie's digs and we kissed beneath the mistletoe that hung from the hall light. 'You're frozen,' said Sadie.

'Better now,' I said. 'Much better.'

The sitting room glittered with gold and silver decorations. Paper chains formed a shimmering cross from corner to corner. The walls bristled with holly wreaths and bells like cardboard concertinas hung on either side of the mirror. 'Fancy a tot of rum?' asked Mr Carrington. He had served in the navy during the First World War and his drinking tastes had been formed then. He stood with his back to the fire, glass in hand, and patted his stomach. 'It brings out the navel spirit,' he said. 'D'you get it? N.a.v.e.l.'

Mrs Carrington offered me a box of chocolate liqueurs. There were rows of miniature bottles; kirsch and curaçao, framboise and crème de menthe. I shook my head. 'Not just now, thanks.'

The heat and the dazzle of reflected light made me feel giddy and for an instant I had the impression of standing in front of a furnace which we were all stoking with our hopes and good intentions, as if we could purge ourselves of every old unhappiness in the blaze. Then I remembered my mother in the house which I had left only a few hours earlier and I knew that it was not possible.

I took the glass that was offered to me and drained it in one gulp. 'Merry Christmas,' said Mr Carrington.

Four

MY DAUGHTER Alice was born the following Easter. Emma wrote to me from the hospital and added a shaky post-script: 'Mother feeling fine but not eager to repeat the performance.'

I told no one all day, but that evening I showed the letter to Sadie. She read it impassively, then handed it back. 'I'm glad it's not me.'

'I thought you wanted children.'

'Not yet. Not like that.'

'Don't you worry about them,' I said. 'They'll manage.'

Sadie shook her head. 'I don't want simply to manage. I want something better.'

It was not the first time she had made such a remark; living with the Carringtons was having its effect. It began with Sadie wearing Dodie's clothes. One bitterly cold day Mrs Carrington urged her to try on a coat which, she said, had been bought the previous winter and hardly worn. 'It's such a waste,' she said. 'It's just hanging there attracting moths.' The coat was bottle green with a high collar and deep pockets and fitted Sadie perfectly. At first she demurred, but then accepted it and now wore it constantly.

'Don't you feel funny?' I asked.

'Not really. And it makes them feel better.'

The coat was succeeded by a pair of shoes, then a dress and then a handbag. I saw the expression on Mrs Carrington's face as Sadie paraded for their inspection before going out and my uneasiness grew. 'Don't you think the colour suits her?' she said. 'I always liked Dodie in green.'

'It's a magical colour,' I said. 'Magicians used to wear

it. I was reading about it the other day.'

Mrs Carrington brushed a speck of lint from Sadie's shoulder. 'I don't know anything about that.' She stood back to admire her grooming. 'Don't you think that skirt's a wee bit short?' she enquired.

Sadie squinted down at her legs, back and front. 'Is it?'

'I don't think so,' I said.

'You weren't being asked,' said Mrs Carrington sweetly. 'Men have no idea. They don't know about fashion.'

Mr Carrington slapped me on the back. 'All we know is how to pay for it. Isn't that right.'

'I suppose so.'

'No doubt about it.' Mr Carrington laughed uproari-ously and jingled the coins in his trouser pocket. 'Cash on the nail. That's all you need to know.'

It was a topic which I did my best to avoid. Since Christmas I had become acutely aware of how much the Carringtons were contributing to my welfare. I was not only a fixture at Sunday lunch, but whenever Sadie and I went out in the evening they left supper on the table to await our return. Recently Mrs Carrington had taken to leaving a packet of cigarettes on the tray which I was expected to take home with me. One evening there were no cigarettes and when I searched for them I realised that I was beginning to take for granted a pattern of comforts and favours which had evolved without my noticing it.

'It's nothing to them,' said Sadie, when I told her how awkward it made me feel. 'They can afford it and they like doing it.'

'But there's nothing I can give them back.'

'They don't expect anything.'

'They expect you to be like Dodie.'

'What harm is there in that?'

'You ought to be yourself.'

'I am,' said Sadie. 'I haven't changed inside. I don't feel any different.'

'You act differently,' I said. 'I notice it all the time.'

Although I frequently tried to persuade her, Sadie would no longer come back with me to my room. It was too scary, she said; she dreamed of Minnie and Lily lying in wait. But the reasons, I suspected lay elsewhere. Gradually, Sadie was becoming the daughter the Carringtons wanted her to be. Her laugh was less shrill. She wore shoes with lower heels. The new clothes she bought (with coupons supplemented by Mrs Carrington) were subdued. It was almost as though her body was wilting beneath layers of good taste.

Sometimes we tried to make love in the sitting room with the lights off and the electric fire shining on Sadie's bare shoulders. But neither of us were relaxed and I longed for good weather when we could lie out of doors. 'It's all you ever think about,' complained Sadie.

'Of course it isn't.'

'You could start thinking about what we're going to do when you go in the army.'

'How d'you mean?'

'Shall we get engaged? With a ring and everything?'

Although marriage, like a dream landscape, had always hovered somewhere ahead of us, I had never seriously considered taking the intermediate step. 'If you like,' I said.

'You don't sound very keen.'

'Yes I am.'

'I don't want to rush you into anything. Let's think about it for a while.'

I thought instead of Emma. It was what she had warned me against but I could never tell Sadie what she had said. 'All right then. I won't be eighteen till next January. We can make up our minds before then.'

'Don't strain yourself,' said Sadie.

'What's wrong? Isn't that what you wanted?'

'I've not much choice.'

Her irritation was undisguised, but at first I could not see what made her angry. Slowly it dawned on me. I had agreed too soon. There was no doubt that Sadie wanted to regularise her position. It was sensible for us to deliberate on whether or not we should become engaged. But she was insulted when I accepted her suggestion without demurring. I should have let myself be coaxed into being cautious. Playing safe was her prerogative, not mine.

I was not sure how our new reflective state affected our plans for a holiday. The Carringtons had already announced their intention of taking Sadie with them to Bournemouth in July, but Sadie herself had decided to pay a return visit to the Homes earlier in the summer. It was not because of her fondness for the place, or out of a perverse sense of nostalgia. Girls who came up to their own expectations or, better still, surpassed them after leaving the Homes frequently went back to show themselves off to those who remained. It reassured them of their own status and, coincidentally, raised the hopes of the stragglers.

There was also a particular pleasure in breaking the rules they once had to obey. Make-up was applied with a heavy hand. Smoking was done with a dash. There was surreptitious drinking. Old flames were inspected and rejected once again. For as long as the stay lasted, one world could be compared with another. And there was the sublime moment to look forward to on the day of departure when, with the bus about to drive south, there came the reminder that there would be no let or hindrance. The escape route was still open.

I did not share Sadie's enthusiasm for the trip but when she asked me to go with her I agreed, chiefly because the Carringtons opposed it. Mrs Carrington, in particular, felt that our travelling together implied a state of affairs which was not proper.

'What do you suppose people will think?' she demanded. 'It almost looks as though you're husband and wife.'

Sadie tossed back her hair, a habit that had intensified as her page-boy bob had grown longer. 'They'll soon find out that we're not.'

'That's even worse.'

'Steady on, Mother,' said Mr Carrington, who had spent some time the day before explaining how broadminded he was. 'It's none of our business.'

'I don't know what is then. If you care about someone, you care about the impression they give. Sadie knows I'm not interfering; just saying what I think.'

'People up there already know us,' said Sadie. 'They won't get the wrong idea.'

'It's nothing to do with them anyway,' I said.

Mrs Carrington sipped her tea with a pained expression. 'I can see you've made your minds up. You must do as you think best.'

She managed to give the impression that she had spent the night deliberating over the advice which we had rejected out of hand and I wondered, not for the first time, if she had exerted the same moral leverage on Dodie. It was sad that her daughter had been killed, but I could not believe that their relationship had been as serene as she implied. Mrs Carrington made me feel like an imposter. I was grateful for her kindness and, to make myself agreeable, I found myself deferring to her and pretending to share views and attitudes which I thought detestable. She gave freely, but not without strings. We were expected to follow guidelines which she laid down and any disagreement constituted a revolt.

'That suits me,' I told Sadie. 'I didn't come to London to be bossed about by someone I hardly know. Nor did you.'

'It's different when you live under the same roof,' she said.

'Maybe you should move.'

'I can't do that.'

'You mean you don't want to.'

'That's right,' said Sadie. 'I'm not moving from where I'm welcome when there's no need.'

She was as stubborn as me, but she made her stand without any of the bluster which I sometimes found necessary. Her calmness was as soothing as milk, but she could be obdurate when she chose. She did not insist on having her own way if someone else's way suited her equally well. But if she decided to the contrary she could not be budged.

A month before we were due to go to the Homes the war in Europe ended. There were street parties and in house after house, whole windows blossomed with Union Jacks. On VE Day Sadie and I joined the crowds in the Mall and danced in front of the railings at Buckingham Palace. At home, Mr Carrington poured huge tots of rum and toasted the King. Then, staring fixedly ahead as though he had seen a vision through the embossed fleur-de-lys of the wallpaper, he sang the National Anthem from beginning to end. The performance exhausted him. He sat down heavily in his fawn leather armchair and pointed to the bottle. There was no need for words. I refilled his glass and then my own.

'It's a wonderful day,' he said. 'There'll be mothers giving thanks all over the world. Their sons are coming home. We shall see peace in our time. No more blackout. An end to rationing. And Jimmy will go to sleep in his own little room again.'

It was another cue for song. Mr Carrington launched into The White Cliffs of Dover, but half way through it he was overcome by emotion. 'Wonderful for you,' he said, gripping my shoulder. 'No one shooting at you. No more foreign parts. Bluebirds all over.' I disengaged myself and backed away as he collapsed in a contented heap.

'Of course,' said Mrs Carrington. 'He's not quite right is he? There's still the other business.'

'Soon be over and done with,' I said.

Mrs Carrington studied me wisely over the rim of her glass. 'You hope.'

She was right. I hoped with all my heart that the Japanese would surrender or be driven into the sea. I imagined the jungle war too vividly to make light of it, but there was also the uncomfortable sense of joining a game in its closing minutes. The first players on the field would be the last to leave and I could already see myself, bored and redundant in the fading light, as the touchline emptied of spectators.

I had not heard from Harry for several weeks and it seemed likely that he had been posted overseas. But the day that we travelled north on our visit to the Homes, a letter arrived saying that he was still at Ringway camp, near Manchester.

'We could all meet while we're up there,' said Sadie.

'D'you really want to?'

'I don't see why not. He's a friend.'

'Too much of a friend sometimes. You let him make a meal of it.'

Sadie wrinkled her nose. 'What a horrible expression!'

'Anyway,' I said. 'He can't take leave when he feels like it. The army says whether he can go or not.'

'You should keep in touch,' said Sadie virtuously. 'That's what friends are for.'

I was struck by a suspicion that fast hardened into a certainty. 'Has he been keeping in touch with you?'

'He's sent me a couple of cards.'

'You never told me.'

'It wasn't important. Cards don't count.'

As I had already noticed, Sadie had her own set of rules which she could fit to any given circumstance. Her dealings with the Carringtons were governed by convenience. Her relationship with me was sustained by habit as much as it was by affection. She was provident but she was also sentimental; cautious, but prone to sudden impulse. If she said that cards did not count she had already convinced herself that this was so.

'You can send him a card when we get there,' I said. 'We'll both sign it.'

'If you like.' Sadie's way of disposing of an argument was to surround it with indifference. It was like punching at flies. The waste of energy was demoralising.

The train to Manchester was crowded. The corridor was jammed with troops and their equipment and Sadie was offered a kit-bag to sit on. We were separated by the length of the carriage, but I could hear her laugh slicing through the racket of the wheels and occasionally I caught a glimpse of her face, pink with pleasure, as she exchanged backchat with a group of Royal Engineers. It was useless trying to join her so I turned my back and watched the country slide by the window. I had made the journey so often that most of the route was familiar. I could anticipate particular streets and houses. I knew the patterns of their curtains – plain in winter, flowered in summer – and I could predict at which point in which county the colour of the door-steps was about to change from rust red to sulphur yellow. I tried to read the cinema posters, stuck to gable ends, as we rattled past. Films took two or three months to travel the circuits after their London opening and it was like flipping backwards through a diary as I remembered when I had first seen them.

It was late July and there were poppies in the corn fields. When we passed a factory close to Stafford I saw girls leaning out of the windows, their hair tied up in turbans, their bare arms flashing as they waved to the train. We crossed a viaduct and the river that wound below dazzled in the sun. I smelled cut grass and saw haymakers leaning on their rakes while a horse dozed between the shafts of the wagon. Living in London I missed the turning of the year. I watched the leaves fatten and fall. I noticed flowers in the parks. But the quickening of each season and its end was less perceptible than it had been in the country.

I had forgotten how much country there was. At Manchester we changed trains for Bolton and from there, caught the bus to the Homes. The town dwindled into suburbs, then into villages and then there were long, empty stretches of road with tracks reaching up to farms lodged on the flanks of the moor. Driving through the valleys we passed mills built of red brick with tall, fuming chimneys. But they were like toys in the landscape. Fields and moorland lay on every side beneath a pale blue sky. They were divided by drystone walls, patched with lichen, but the boundaries were like scratches made by thorns on an enormous hide. The marks were temporary. In time the land would shrug them off. The pelt would renew itself and life would go on, unperturbed and unchanging. Nothing that had happened in the past four years had made any impression here. The war was of no consequence. The same grasses grew, the same rain fell. It was like looking on eternity and I was glad that I had gone away.

Sadie had arranged for me to stay at a cottage about a mile from the Homes, but the bus made its turn outside the governor's house and as we got off, cases in hand, Mr Rome, the governor, was crossing the road. We could not avoid each other. He began to offer his hand, then withdrew it and nodded stiffly. 'You're not staying at the branch, I take it.'

'No. I'm up the road.'

'That's just as well.' He stared at me hard and sighed. 'You've caused a great deal of trouble.'

'I'm sorry,' I said.

'I very much doubt it. You're a great disappointment. You let down everyone.'

'Sister Emma doesn't think so.'

He raised a finger as if to seal my lips. 'We won't discuss Sister Emma. As far as the branch is concerned she resigned for reasons of health. I want no gossip while you're here. I rely on you to be discreet. For her sake, if not your own.'

'There's no one I'm likely to talk to,' I said. 'I won't be here long.'

'Very well.' Mr Rome bobbed his head like a bird pecking up crumbs. 'And what about that young woman?' He indicated Sadie who was waiting for me across the road.

'You needn't worry about her.'

'You're sure?'

'Certain.'

'What I fail to understand is why you came back at all,' he said. 'You can't have imagined you'd be welcome.'

The truth was that I had not really considered it. I had accompanied Sadie because she had asked me to. But when I measured my reasons they amounted to little more than a shoddy compound of petulance and bravado.

'The decent thing would have been to have stayed away,' said Mr Rome. 'You've brought nothing but unhappiness.'

It was as though, without warning, I had tuned in to another waveband on the wireless. Mr Rome was not simply sad; he was also peevish. I heard not only regret for what had happened, but irritation that it had caused him personal inconvenience. I stopped apologising. 'Emma's not unhappy,' I said. 'She's glad she has the baby.'

Mr Rome clicked his tongue disbelievingly. 'Don't be absurd.'

'She told me so. She has everything planned. She knows exactly what she's going to do.'

I saw Sadie look sharply in my direction and I realised that I had raised my voice. 'There's no need to shout,' said Mr Rome.

'There's no need for you to feel hard done by,' I said.

There was a moment's pause in which the breeze flicked our faces and I heard the ring of the conductor's bell as the bus began its return journey. It rolled by us in a funnel of dust. 'That's quite enough from you,' said Mr Rome. 'It's time you were on your way.'

He turned on his heel and walked briskly up the steps to his front door. His shoes, I noticed, were as beautifully polished as ever. Beneath the dust which the bus had blown over them they shone like freshly peeled conkers. He shut the door behind him with a bang and I picked up my suitcase. 'What was all that about?' asked Sadie.

'It doesn't matter.'

'Were you having a row?'

'He was telling me what a mess I'd made of things. Especially for him.'

Sadie put her hand on my arm. 'You can't blame him for being narky. You were one of his pets. That makes it worse.'

'There's no point in him going on about it. It won't change anything.'

'Nothing changes here,' said Sadie. She turned round in a complete circle, reviewing the world we had left behind. Wisps of hay trailed from the portholes of the barn. The laundry chimney flew its flag of steam. I noticed fresh paint on the doors and windows of Mosscrop House where I had lived when I first came to the branch and there was a new girl at the window of the office where Sadie had worked. But the same wind-bowed lilacs stood on the corner. The milk cooler hummed its familiar tune in the dairy and at the bend in the road I saw a boy with a broom listlessly pushing a scrap of paper along the gutter. I had often done the same job myself on Saturdays when I took my turn on The Shop, the branch's casual work force.

'We've changed,' I said. 'They can't get me doing that any more.'

It was small consolation. Mr Rome was right in one respect; I had not assumed that I would be welcome. But I had been wrong in thinking it did not matter. In coming back I was not playing Sadie's game of parading my success for the admiration of those who remained. But part of me, I now realised, hungered for approval. It was unimportant who gave it. What I looked for was a general blessing; a climate, almost, in which the forecast was hopeful, the outlook benign. I surprised myself by wanting it and I understood why Harry protected himself against injury and disappointment by caring about nothing. He wore his indifference like armour. He was not to be admired; but at that moment I envied him.

We stayed at the Homes for three days. The cottage in which I rented a room belonged to a widower with two daughters who had attended school at the Homes, but who now worked in a factory near Bolton where they made army tents. His name was Chambers. He had a small dairy herd and several goats whose milk he made into soft white cheese. It scented the whole house; sour and mild as if something was gently decomposing beneath the floorboards.

Mr Chambers ate it at every meal, dreamily licking the pale crumbs out of his moustache and washing them down with mug after mug of strong tea. 'My girls wanted to go to London,' he told me at breakfast. 'I told 'em Bolton was far enough away. They come home at weekends. Not every week. But when they can. They're good girls. They do as they're told.'

I thought it unlikely, but said nothing. Photographs of Mr Chambers' daughters were propped up on the mantelpiece. They looked big and bold, with thick black eyebrows and their hair piled on their heads. It was combed up on either side in soft horns and clamped into position with slides. I remembered them from my first weeks at school. Their names were Rose and Marigold. Their mother, they said, had been fond of flowers, but they were too high on the moors to make any kind of a garden. The soil was poor, and strong winds shattered the blossom.

Mr Chambers had never travelled further from home than Blackburn. 'There's no point,' he said. 'Why should I go traipsing all over the place? It's better here than in London with all them air raids.'

'They've stopped now. We've beaten the Germans.'

He sucked the fringe of his moustache as if he was extracting the very essence of the cheese he had just eaten. 'They never dropped a bomb up here. Safe as houses, we were.' His face folded into an expression of extreme craftiness, so exaggerated that it was like a cartoon.

'You could be bored to death,' I said.

'There's plenty to do.'

I looked through the fly-specked window on to fields where black and white cows moonily chewed the cud. I had volunteered to wash out the shippon after milking. Then, if I wanted to, I could chop wood for the fire that evening when Sadie was coming to supper. Or I could look for the eggs that one of the hens had been laying away from the coop. Or I could drown a litter of kittens newly discovered in the barn. There was a

variety of ways in which I could pass the time, but I
found few of them appealing. Mr Rome had told me
to stay away from the Homes which meant, in effect,
that I was also barred from seeing Sadie while she remained there. It was a pity, I thought, that Mrs Carrington
did not know what the situation was. It would have
given her unexpected satisfaction.

We had eggs and bacon for supper and then I walked
Sadie back to the Homes leaving Mr Chambers with a
virgin cheese in front of him and his pruning knife open.
'Sure you won't have a nibble?' he asked.

'No thank you.'

'Nothing like this in London,' he said, making the
first incision.

There was a moon, as white as the cheese, blazing
down on the moor. We walked towards it until we were
above the reservoir, shifting and glinting between dark
beds of heather. Owls cried along the valley and looking
towards the sound I saw, for the first time in years, the
squares and oblongs of windows stripped of their blackout and shining into the night.

I thought of them months later on VJ Day when Sadie
and I were jammed in an Underground train that had
stuck in a tunnel half a mile short of the Angel. The
lights across the valley had been a declaration of peace,
but this was the real thing. The pubs had been open
since early in the morning and many of the passengers
were drunk. There were two sailors standing behind me,
their heads angled forward by the carriage roof. The
shorter of the two was very pale. I watched beads of
sweat pop up on his forehead as though they were being
squeezed through muslin and I realised that he was going
to be sick.

'There you go, mate,' said his friend, tipping off the
small sailor's hat and holding it neatly under his chin.
He was just in time. The reek of vomit was added to
the smells of sweat and spilled beer. The train staggered

forward a few yards, then stopped. The lights flickered and went out and the woman standing beside me screamed. 'Don't worry, love,' said the sailor who had taken care of his friend, 'it won't be for long.' He was mistaken. We remained in the tunnel for another hour. For the first fifteen minutes there was an attempt to organise a sing-song. Matches and cigarette lighters were lit and in the rosy glow I remembered once, before my mother was taken ill, going the rounds as a carol singer bearing a candle in a jam-jar, suspended on string.

In the tunnel it was less convivial. We sang *Roll Out the Barrel* and *We'll Meet Again* and then the woman who had screamed crumpled up like an empty sock and by slow degrees sank towards the floor. She did not reach it because we were packed together too tightly. I tried to lift her but she was a dead weight and lolled between our knees as if her body was saturated by the foul air. Someone shouted 'Put that light out', the catch-phrase of Air Raid Wardens during the war. But no one laughed and, one by one, the matches and cigarette lighters were extinguished and the darkness became absolute.

'Harry'll be wondering where we are,' said Sadie.

'He won't go away.'

The previous night Harry had phoned to say that he had forty-eight hours leave and we had arranged to meet him in a pub off City Road. Work had ended early because of the celebrations. There had been very little business at any of the courts. Fines had been light and case after case had been adjourned. Sadie and I met at Blackfriars after I had delivered the day's copy to the offices of the nationals and walked up Fleet Street and into Trafalgar Square where a five-piece band played Dixieland jazz. Two of the musicians were GIs; the others were civilians. The trumpet player climbed on to the balustrade opposite the National Portrait Gallery and played the opening bars of *Maryland* before falling into the arms of the crowd below. They set him back on his feet and he resumed playing where he had left off.

Someone gave me a bottle of port and I was left holding

it when the crowd twitched like the skin of an animal and shrugged away. People seemed to be incapable of moving independently. They formed choirs, teams, chains of dancers who held hands or embraced from one side of the square to the other, so that there was contact, or more often, communion between men and women standing twenty yards apart. It was like swimming with someone else's arms or walking with someone else's feet. A man wearing a bowler hat festooned with red, white and blue rosettes tapped Sadie on the shoulder and when she turned, he politely raised his bowler and kissed her on the lips. Then, with equal ceremony, he kissed me too. I handed him the bottle and as he tilted his head back to drink from it the crowd bore him away and he disappeared from view, the bottle still poised like a periscope above the sea of bobbing heads.

We struggled back into Charing Cross Road and fought our way into the Underground. Twenty minutes later we were trapped in the tunnel. Either the lack of oxygen or the abrupt end to the excitement of the streets drained us of energy. We spoke in whispers. The woman pinned between our knees stirred once or twice, but made no attempt to get up.

'Won't be long now,' said the tall sailor. 'Bit like being in a sub. Nothing to worry about. Power failure probably.'

'Have you been in a sub?' asked Sadie.

'Never,' said the sailor. 'Don't think I want to now.'

It was a funny way to celebrate the end of a war, I thought, bottled up beneath a London pavement and imagining what it was like being in a submarine. But it seemed appropriate. I had almost been bombed. I had almost had to fight a terrifying enemy. And because I had been spared on both counts I was luckier than many of my generation. But, as I had anticipated, peace was proving to be an anticlimax and it had only just begun.

It was a depressing thought and I could not shake it off, even after we had been released from the train and found Harry in the pub. 'For Christ's sake, cheer up,' he said. 'We've won the war, not lost it.'

'He's been like it all night,' said Sadie. 'I don't know what's wrong with him.'

Harry rolled down my eyelids and put an ear to my chest. 'He needs a drink. Leave it to Uncle Harry.' He pushed his glass towards me. 'Try this.'

It looked like beer, but there was another flavour which I could not identify. 'What is it?'

'Dog's Nose,' said Harry.

'What's that?'

He ordered a pint of bitter and waited until I had lowered it by half an inch, then added a single gin. 'You keep topping it up,' he explained.

I sipped it cautiously, but there was no ill effect. 'It's a great drink,' said Harry.

'Great,' I said. It was a pleasant pub, I decided. There were rows of horse brasses behind the bar, so closely hung together that they resembled solid seams of metal. The windows and the lamp-shades bristled with Union Jacks and perched on one of the beer pumps was a parrot. Its plumage was red and grey and it regarded me with eyes as yellow as a toe-nail.

'That's Cocky,' said Harry.

I offered it my finger and quite deliberately the parrot bit it. The landlord rapped on the bar top and pointed to a notice between the brasses. 'It is Forbidden to Feed the Animals,' he recited.

Sadie shrieked with laughter and Harry ordered another round of drinks. The level in my glass never seemed to go down appreciably although I had kept pace with everyone else's drinking. My depression had gone and I was filled with a wonderful confidence which ir-radiated me like an electric fire. I could feel every bone, every vein glowing. 'I have perfect circulation,' I an-nounced. 'My mother says I'm as warm as toast.'

'Your mother!' said Sadie.

'There's nothing wrong with my mother.'

'That's not what I've heard,' said Harry. He was wear-ing his beret and his jumping suit and he looked even more rakish than I remembered. I wanted to ask him whether there was anything he cared about which would soften his judgement or make him change his mind, but I could not formulate the question in any way that made sense. The brasses behind the bar shone brightly. The parrot cocked its head. The floor came up to meet me. I felt myself being lifted by my elbows as though I was an armchair and found myself sitting on the pavement with my back to the wall.

'Are you all right?' asked Sadie.

'Perfect.'

'Pissed,' said Harry. 'I've never seen it happen so fast.' His voice came and went as if it was on the end of a cord which he was swinging round his head. When it went away I strained to hear what he was saying; when it was close to me I was deafened. I wanted to go to sleep, but when I lay down they lifted me up and when I was on my feet I felt so sick that I knew I was going to die.

We walked the two miles to my digs. We passed policemen that I knew and policemen I thought I knew and it seemed to me of paramount importance that we should say goodnight to each and every one. If I was arrested and appeared in the dock instead of the press box I wanted my courtesy to be on record. When we reached my front door Harry unlocked it with the key he found in my pocket and led me to the foot of the stairs. He pointed into the darkness above us and I crawled towards it. The climb was long and punctuated by several little naps but at the end of it I found my own door and, eventually, my bed.

I awoke to Minnie pounding on the door to tell me it was time to go to work. I felt terrible. My mouth was parched, my head ached and, worst of all, the world slid away when I looked at it. All morning I held on to things and it was not until noon that equilibrium returned. I spent the day at North London. Frank Maitland was standing in for Tim and as the long parade of drunks filed through the court he studied a small text book and wrote lists of words on his pad of copy paper.

I studied it curiously. Some of the words seemed familiar, but they obviously belonged to another language. 'Esperanto,' said Frank. 'They could do with it here. They'd need no interpreters then.' It would be one of the tools of the new society, he told me later; the language of an international brotherhood.

'Is it easy to learn?'

'Not only easy,' said Frank. 'Essential.'

We were in the jailer's office, copying a new batch of charge sheets. 'Useful for the hairy-arsed ones,' said Sergeant Collins. 'Instant communication when you're telling them they're nicked.'

Frank shook his head. 'There'd be fewer arrests.'

'How's that?'

'There'd be less misunderstanding. Less reason for punch-ups.'

Sergeant Collins turned the pages of his ledger inscribed with the names of the day's defendants; the first defaulters in a brave new world. 'You've got a hope,' he said. 'People don't change.'

I did not see Harry before he went back to camp and Sadie left word with the Carringtons that she was working late at the office to make up for the time lost during the VJ celebrations. It was odd, I thought. She had not warned me that she was likely to have to do overtime.

'She can't be expected to tell you everything,' said Mrs Carrington.

'I've not asked her to.'

'She's got her own life to live.'

'I know that,' I said. 'It's just that I'm going to be busy this weekend.'

I had arranged to see Emma at Sally Derby's house where she was staying for a few days. We had written to each other regularly and she had sent me photographs of Alice, but I was still unable to grasp the fact that I was the father of a child who looked, Emma insisted, remarkably like me. At first I could not see the resemblance. She lay wedged between cushions on Sally's settee, waving her fists at the ceiling.

'You can pick her up if you like,' said Emma. 'She won't come apart.'

Gingerly, I did as she suggested. Alice smelled of milk and talcum powder. Bubbles like beads of cuckoo-spit boiled between her lips and I saw the top of her head throb alarmingly as if by some bizarre accident her heart lay just below her scalp. I touched the place that pulsed so steadily and felt a gap, covered only by skin and hair like the down on a day-old chick.

'The bones haven't joined up yet,' said Emma. 'It's perfectly normal.'

'I'm glad to hear it.'

'What do you think of her?'

'Beautiful,' I said. 'She's a lovely girl.'

'She's the best thing that ever happened to me,' said Emma. 'I can't think what I did without her.'

I felt an enormous relief as if what had threatened to be a disaster had turned into a triumph. I had a share in the first part, but not the second. 'D'you really mean it?'

Emma took the baby from my arms. 'Of course I do.' She wiped away the bubbles and watched them well up again. 'She's all mine,' she said. 'no one can take her away from me.'

I thought how wrong Mr Rome had been, but said nothing. I felt warmed by Emma's happiness. It was like stepping out of a dark room into the blaze of noon. There were no shadows, no uncertainties. I saw love like sunlight, clear and unconditional. 'She's yours too,' said Emma. 'I want you to remember that.'

'I will.'

The peace meant something after all, I thought. Not to me, but to someone who would make use of it. I wondered, irrelevantly, if Alice would learn to speak Esperanto, the language of the brave new world. I touched her cheek and Emma covered my hand with hers. 'Things will work out,' she said, and I believed her.

Five

AT THE END of my first week in the army I dropped my rifle during arms drill. Between the orders for 'Slope' and 'Present Arms' my fingers lost their grip and my Browning 303 ('The soldier's best friend' advised the sergeant instructor) clattered to the tarmac.

The sergeant, a weary veteran of the Rhine Army, turned his head and studied the skyline. His demob number was coming up soon and, as he frequently reminded us, all he wanted to do was serve the rest of his time without drama, cockups or the necessity of having to put any of us on a fizzer. We warmed to his indifference, but a young second lieutenant – newly commissioned and eager to show how gravely I had offended his sense of military decorum – dashed his swagger stick to the parade ground and actually danced up and down in his rage.

I felt myself blushing. 'I'm sorry,' I said.

The lieutenant paused. 'What d'you mean, sorry?'

'Sorry, *sir*,' I said.

He quivered all over as if someone was shaking him from inside. 'Don't say you're sorry. Pick it up. Come to attention. Raise your weapon over your head and double round the parade ground!'

I trotted off while he screamed at me now and again in what we both took to be a soldierly fashion. I did not find it upsetting. Learning to be a soldier was pretty much as I had imagined it would be. It was no worse than the Bluecoat school and it was considerably more agreeable than being at the Homes. The rules were absurd and the bullshit was boring, but of all the institutions I had known it seemed to me the most relaxed, and apart from twerps like the lieutenant and ogres like the Regimental Sergeant Major who roared in the distance and instilled terror by his reputation alone, I enjoyed the company.

I was called up three months after my eighteenth birthday and my departure was a modest occasion. I had a farewell drink with Frank Maitland and Tim Mocock, and Eric presented me with a testimonial in which he said I had 'character, self-reliance and that element of personal charm which is of value to a journalist.'

'Come in handy, that will,' said Sergeant Collins, who had threatened to write to my commanding officer, warning him what to expect. 'Nothing like personal charm in the face of the enemy.'

'There is no enemy now.'

'I was forgetting,' said Sergeant Collins, who forgot nothing. 'Peace-time soldiering's different.'

On the appointed day I was ordered to report to Warley Barracks in Essex by three o'clock in the afternoon. Waiting for the train I saw several other solitary figures nursing suitcases and guessed rightly that they too were bound for the army. We identified ourselves and crammed into one compartment. There was a trainee solicitor's clerk, a builder's labourer, a barber, an electrician's mate, an accountant and a boy who sat in the opposite corner hugging a brown paper parcel. He was either shy or frightened, I thought. He had curly black hair and an olive skin and although it was early April and still chilly he wore no overcoat; only a thin black sweater with holes at each elbow.

'What's your name?' I asked.

He shied away as if I had threatened him with my fist. 'David.'

'Is that your surname?'

He shook his head. 'David Williams.'

'D'you come from London?'

'Holloway.'

'I've been living at Highbury,' I said. 'That's just five minutes away.'

He did not seem at all interested. 'I live with my mum.

And my dog. They shouldn't have got me to come here.'

He looked around him indignantly and gripped his parcel as if he was afraid one of us might snatch it from him. 'I never wanted to,' he said. 'I wanted to stay with my mum.'

'Didn't we all,'said the barber whose name was Sims.

'My mum didn't want me to go,' said Williams. 'She told the bobby when he came. But he said I had to. They were going to lock me up otherwise.'

It was like listening to an event being described by a small child who understood nothing of what had occurred. 'Everybody gets called up,' I said. 'You're not being treated any differently.'

He shook his head. 'I was up all night with the dog. He kept crying. He knew I was going off.'

'What sort of dog is it?'

'Brown,' he said. 'With white paws.'

'What breed?'

He shook his head again. 'He's called Prince.'

For the rest of the journey he remained silent and when we piled into the lorry which took us to the barracks he squatted on the floor and stared at his shoes. The soles had parted from the uppers and they were laced up with string. Over the next couple of hours I saw Williams being shouted at, herded into line and once being led by his hand from one desk to another by a succession of NCOs who treated him rather like a casualty in a bombing raid who had escaped obvious injury, but whose incomprehension was a wound which excited both their pity and their rage.

'He's barmy,' said Sims. 'Thick as two planks!'

'Working his ticket, more like,' said Dollimore, the electrician's mate. 'Good luck to him if he can pull it off.'

I watched Williams drop his trousers for the MO and his look of outrage when it was explained what was required of him. Sulkily he coughed when he was told to, but there was no mistaking the impression he conveyed of offence given and offence received. 'My mum said not to let people touch me,' he explained when I asked what had gone wrong.

'You're going to get a lot of that.'

'No I won't,' he said. 'I shall tell my mum. She'll put a stop to it.'

I looked at him sharply, half expecting to catch the last flicker of a grin. But he seemed completely serious. There was no trace of a smile. He clasped the brown paper parcel to his chest and I caught the whiff of moth balls.

'What's in there?'

'My things.'

'What things?'

'Combinations. They were my dad's. My mum says I have to wear them.' He peeled back one edge of the parcel and showed me layers of yellow wool, seeded with small rubber buttons.

'You can't wear comb's in the army,' I said. 'They won't let you.'

Williams carefully remade his parcel. 'I didn't want to come here in the first place,' he said. 'It's their fault if it all goes wrong.'

Our barrack room was small and dirty, with an iron stove at one end of the room and rows of wooden bunks facing each other across the splintered floor. On each bunk there lay a pile of three straw-filled biscuits. 'You put them end to end to make your mattress,' said the corporal. 'Any fleas you find you brought with you.'

'Prince had fleas,' Williams told me with a sigh. 'I had to stop having him in my bed.'

He had taken the bunk beneath mine and during the night I awoke to hear him crying in his sleep. His face was quite peaceful, but I saw tears striping his cheek. At reveille the next morning he remained curled beneath his blankets and when the corporal stripped them back we saw that he was lying in a pool of urine.

'You dirty little sod. You've just done that,' said the corporal. 'It's still steaming.'

Williams nodded agreeably. 'I always do it if I'm not woken up. My mum wakes me up at home.'

The corporal bent down until his mouth was barely

an inch from Williams' ear. 'Your mum's not here now!' he roared. 'Get out of that bloody scratcher. Take those biscuits back to stores and tell Q what a disgusting little soldier you've been. Then report back to me and we'll decide whether or not to put you on a fizzer.'

The fizzer was deferred but after Williams had wet the bed on four successive nights he was charged with the wilful damage of army property, confined to barracks and ordered to make restitution by weekly instalments deducted from his pay. He was also issued with a rubber sheet which he wiped down with disinfectant every morning. Our corner of the barrack room began to smell like a hospital.

'Why don't you report sick,' I said.

'I'm not ill.'

'But you keep peeing the bed. There must be something wrong.'

'I've already told you,' said Williams, 'all I need is someone to wake me up. My mum wakes me up at home.'

Our initial training at Warley Barracks lasted for six weeks and from first to last Williams maintained a level of inefficiency which seemed likely to establish a record. Like me he dropped his rifle, not once but a dozen times. Without effort he could disrupt a morning's drill by failing, again and again, to distinguish his right foot from his left. He was banned from grenade practice after the sergeant had to prise the grenade from his hand and hurl it into the sand-pit where it exploded with only seconds to spare. He was denied leave. He spent hours in sweeping the barracks and toiling through cookhouse fatigues. He lost his small pack, his best battle-dress and his pay-book. While the rest of the intake gradually began to resemble soldiers, boning their boots and weighting their trouser bottoms with lead bracelets so that they hung evenly over their gaiters, Williams continued to look irrevocably unstrung. He seemed to be put together differently from the rest of us. He lacked co-ordination. His beret refused to remain on the tilt over his right eye, but rode back over his curls to form a halo around his unworried face. He was abused, nagged and finally ignored, but he did not complain except to remind whoever was castigating him that his mum would soon sort things out if she was there.

I told Sadie about him on my first weekend leave. 'He sounds simple to me,' she said. 'They should leave him alone.'

'That's what he wants.'

'Bad for discipline,' said Mr Carrington. 'You can't run a rowing boat like that. Everyone has to join the team.'

Seeing me in uniform had revived his service spirit. He was sorry that I had not joined the navy, but he accepted the army as a tolerable second best. Although the war was over, the mood of emergency was slow to recede. There were still massive troop movements and if our convoys drove more than twenty miles from the barracks – a radius within which public reaction had become *blasé* – housewives would still wave and children cheer.

My mother had demanded photographs of me with my platoon and I knew that, by now, they had gone the rounds of family and friends to prove that whatever my shortcomings in the past I had joined the common cause. I was doing what was normal. Sadie, too, kept my photograph in her handbag, protected by a plastic season ticket case. As we sat down to supper she produced pictures of her own, portraits taken in Hyde Park in which she sprawled on the grass and smiled vivaciously against a background of daffodils. No one else appeared in the photographs, but in one of them I noticed the shadow of the photographer stretching from the bottom edge of the picture towards her feet.

'Who took this?' I asked.

She frowned and bit her lip. 'I'm not sure. I don't remember.'

'Yes you do,' said Mrs Carrington, looking over her shoulder. 'That was the day you went out with that other boy in the army. What's his name now?'

'Harry,' I said, and she nodded comfortably as if I

had supplied the answer to a clue in the evening crossword.

Sadie slid the photographs back in their folder. 'Didn't I write and tell you?'

'Not that I remember.'

'It was just the other week. He took me out for a meal.'

'And he came here for lunch,' said Mrs Carrington. 'Quite a nice boy, I thought.'

Mr Carrington poured himself a glass of beer and passed me the bottle. 'What do they call his lot?' he enquired. 'The Red Demons, is it?'

'Red Devils,' I said.

'Will you be joining them?'

'They won't have me. Poor eyesight.'

Mr Carrington sipped his beer and sighed. 'Just as well, I reckon. There's no sense in taking risks if you're not one hundred per cent fit.'

'It's just my eyes,' I said. 'I'm fine otherwise.'

I had been going to tell them about the route marches and the unarmed combat in which the wrestling falls I had learned at school had come in useful. But, measured against Harry's toughness, it sounded like feeble boasting. What I could not understand was why Sadie had pretended not to remember that it was Harry who had taken the photographs. Later that night when the Carringtons had gone to bed I asked her.

'I told you,' she said. 'I forgot.'

'Mrs Carrington didn't forget.'

'I can't help that.'

'There's no need to sulk. I wasn't accusing you of anything.'

'I should hope not,' said Sadie. 'You've got no right. You don't own me.'

Above us the Carringtons continued their usual perambulations. The floor-boards creaked. There was the clink of glass on glass. I heard the bed-springs sigh and settle. It was like listening to the sound-track of a tea-party to which guests had been admitted secretly. I wondered how long they would go on. For the first time Mrs Carrington had invited me to stay the night. I had no digs to go to, she said, and it would be nice for Sadie. A bed had been made up for me in the box-room at the far end of the landing. It was next to Sadie's room, and I planned to visit her when the house had gone to sleep.

'You can't,' said Sadie. 'They'll be listening.'

'Not all night.'

She shook her head resolutely. 'I don't want to upset them.'

'Here, then.'

She rolled her eyes as if I had asked her to perform some tedious chore, then lay beside me on the settee. 'You know you don't like it here.'

I wanted to tell her that after three weeks away in which I had taken unaccustomed exercise, remained celibate and strengthened muscles I never knew I had, I was prepared to like it anywhere. But I deferred to the gentility of the room and we made love swiftly and silently. It was not a great success.

'I told you,' said Sadie.

I accepted the reproach, but then a thought occurred to me. 'Did Harry sleep here?'

'Of course not,' she said. 'He was at the hostel first off. Then he found an hotel.'

'Whereabouts?'

'Up west,' said Sadie. 'Paddington, I think it was.'

'Did you go there?'

'Just for a drink,' she said. 'After he took the photographs.'

'I see.'

'You only see what you want to,' said Sadie. 'You've got a nasty mind. You think everyone's like you.'

'And Harry's not?'

Sadie rolled off the settee and buttoned her blouse. She collected our glasses and a plate on which a ribbon of apple peel was turning brown and took them into the kitchen. I did not follow her. I wished that I had never mentioned Harry. I wished that Sadie had not told me about the hotel in Paddington. I wished that I could rid myself of the memory of that slow and greedy kiss that I had witnessed the time we all went out together. I was glad that I had to be back in camp the following night.

'Did you have a good time?' Williams asked me as I made up my bunk.

'Not bad.'

'Did you see your mum?'

I shook my head. 'I've already told you. She doesn't live in London. I went to see my girl-friend.'

'Don't you want to see your mum?'

'I'd love to but there wasn't time.'

'My mum's the only person in the world I want to see,' said Williams. 'It won't be long now.' He almost crooned the words as if constant repetition had turned them into liturgy. The camp barber had given him a regulation crop, but the new growth which covered his scalp lay in tiny curls as tight as watch springs and I imagined them awaiting a signal, known only to Williams, which would release them so violently that no beret or helmet could possibly contain them. It was like being confronted with an omen.

I smoothed my blankets and made hospital corners. 'Let's hope you're right,' I said.

He smiled swiftly and secretly. 'I'm right,' he said. 'Don't worry about that.'

We were given news of our postings in the last week of the course. I had been turned down not only for the paratroops but also by the War Office Selection Board. 'Let's face it, you're not exactly officer material,' said the lieutenant who had thrown down his swagger stick during arms drill. Instead, I was to join the RASC as a clerk. So was Sims and so was Dollimore. They were both disgusted.

'Bloody pen-pushing,' said Sims.

'What's happened to Williams?' asked Dollimore.

We found him in the barrack room packing his brown

paper parcel into a new fibre-board suitcase. He wore
a skimpy tweed suit and a shirt patterned with thin red
stripes. A trilby hat was perched on the back of his head
and a raincoat was folded neatly across the bottom of
his bunk. 'I'm going home,' he said. 'They've discharged
me.'

Dollimore whistled softly. 'Jammy bugger.'

'On what grounds?' I asked.

Williams smiled, as secretly as usual but with a joy
he found it hard to disguise. 'Compassionate,' he said.
'My mum couldn't cope. She sent a certificate. The doctor
signed it.'

'He'd have signed one for you too,' said Sims. 'Quick
as a flash.'

Williams nodded. 'I expect he would. But there's no
need now.'

'Will your mum be all right?' I asked.

Williams fastened the lock on his suitcase and draped
the raincoat over his arm. 'There's nothing wrong with
my mum. All she needs is me and all I need is her.
I've always told you that. They should never have taken
me away.' He drifted towards the door, then came back
and formally shook our hands. 'Cheerio then,' he said.
'Enjoy yourselves.'

We watched him cross the parade ground. In the distance stood the lieutenant, quivering in anticipation of
a salute. Within seconds he realised that the approaching
target was a civilian, but before he could retreat Williams
swept off his hat and made a low bow. 'Jammy bugger,'
said Dollimore again.

'Crafty, more like,' said Sims.

It was a question we debated all the way to Cirencester
where the army proposed to teach us shorthand and typing. Our camp occupied almost all of Cirencester Park.
It had been an American Air Force hospital and behind
the tawny limestone wall which protected it from the
road lay a complex of Nissen huts, all of them linked
by covered concrete paths. The huts had been wards
and operating theatres. They were clean and spacious

and the floors were made of black plastic which it was easy to polish or swab down. 'There was all that blood to get rid of,' explained our hut corporal. 'Very hygienic, those Yanks.'

The camp, he told us, was haunted by the ghost of an American airman who had died of burns after being shot down. Nightly he patrolled the walkways in his wheelchair, his face swathed in bandages which he would slowly unwind to reveal a charred and blistered horror which, said the corporal, sent anyone who saw it round the bend. 'If you see him coming don't hang about,' he advised us. 'Run like hell.'

Gloucestershire, I decided, was a good deal more pleasant than Essex. I made friends with a jazz drummer from Muswell Hill named Casey Warren who owned a wind-up gramophone on which he played Woody Herman records. Our hero was the trombonist, Bill Harris, whose eccentric solos on *Goosey Gander* and *Apple Honey* Casey would repeat, note for note. He insisted that we learned the tunes and in the mild nights of early summer we marched in a gang to the local pubs chanting Herman instrumentals. By the time we returned to camp the roads were covered with large black slugs which oozed across the macadam like soft shards of an exploded tyre.

It was rumoured that somewhere in the netherland of Nissen huts there was a library and recreation room and after several days exploring I found it. It offered few books, but on a trestle table against the wall there was a selection of magazines. Easy chairs were arranged around the stove and cut-out photographs and illustrations were pinned to the walls. The hut appeared to be empty, but after a while I became aware of a figure leaning on a broom by the door of the NCOs cubicle. He wore a private's uniform, but I noticed that on his feet were civilian brogues and that instead of his tunic being hooked up at the neck, he wore a collar and tie.

I looked up from my notebook and he circled me warily. 'Everything all right?'

'Fine,' I said.

'Were you looking for anything special?'

'Not really. Just somewhere quiet to write a few notes.'

'I see.' He did not seem entirely satisfied. 'Who told you about this place?'

'I forget. Someone happened to mention it.'

He cruised round the hut with his broom, not actually sweeping the floor but stirring the dust so that small puffs of it hung in the sunlight. 'What are you writing?' he asked.

I closed the notebook. 'Bits and pieces.'

'It looked like poetry.'

'Sort of.' In the army it was an admission I had learned not to make lightly.

'Have you published any?'

'Not yet. It's not good enough.'

He propped his broom against the wall of the hut and sat beside me. 'Do you read much?'

'Quite a bit.' I had packed two anthologies but I read them discreetly, as others I had observed read the Bible, before Lights Out or when they believed themselves to be alone.

'Who d'you like best?'

I sensed that I was being tested and it was important to present the right credentials. 'Lawrence,' I said. 'Auden, Sydney Keyes.'

'What about Eliot?'

'Eliot's all right.'

He looked at me pityingly. '*The Waste Land* is the greatest poem in the English language.'

'Not for me.'

'Then you've not read it properly. Stay there.' He dashed into the cubicle by the entrance and emerged with a paperback whose spine had been bound with Sellotape. 'Read it again,' he ordered, thrusting the book into my hand. 'Read it now and tell me if I'm not right.'

He hovered over me while I read the poem, frowning when I went over lines for a second or third time, accepting the book when I had finished as reverently as if I was handing him a splinter of the True Cross.

'Well?' he demanded.

'I see what you mean.'

'Do you really?'

I squirmed in my chair. 'I can see why *you* like it. But there are things I like better.'

He studied me in silence for several seconds, then nodded briskly. 'You'll learn.'

His name, he told me, was Peter Stanford. He was awaiting a posting to the Army Education Corps but when it would come about he had no idea. 'I didn't want them to send me anywhere else in the meantime,' he said, 'so I invented this recreation room.'

'What d'you mean, you invented it?'

'I found it empty. I brought in the chairs and the magazines. Then I made myself the orderly. I've got a billet in the cubicle there. No one bothers me.'

'What if they find out?'

He spread his hands. 'Who's going to find out? People come and go all the time. I can always say I was given the job by someone who was demobbed months ago.'

His exposition was outrageous, but it made perfect sense. 'How long have you been here?' I asked.

'Three months. They come to inspect it once a week and they've even brought me a few books. Trash mostly, but they mean well.'

His manner was a curious mixture of arrogance and enthusiasm. Surrounded by the army on all sides, he had created a miniature world of his own. I looked at the pictures on the walls: photographs by Bill Brandt, reproductions of paintings by Paul Nash and Salvador Dali, a series of drawings by Henry Moore of people sleeping in the Underground, their bodies cocooned like Egyptian mummies. He showed me his cubicle where there were more pictures and row upon row of books. On a table by the bed lay the latest copy of *Penguin New Writing*. Beside it was several issues of *Poetry London*.

'I sent them a batch of my stuff last week,' he said casually. 'It was a toss-up between them and *Horizon*, but I don't think Connolly's keen on my sort of thing.'

I knew that *Horizon* was the most intellectual of the literary magazines and that its editor, Cyril Connolly, had a fearsome reputation as a critic, but I knew nothing of his tastes. 'What sort of thing do you mean?' I asked.

Stanford produced a large folder, bulging with type-written poems. 'I've done these over the last year. The latest are the best. Tell me what you think of them.'

I accepted the folder gingerly. 'Are you sure?'

'Of course I'm sure. You write poetry yourself. I'd like to see something of yours.'

'I've got nothing with me.'

'Bring it round any time. Make use of the place.' He surveyed the snug cubicle with satisfaction. 'What d'you think of it?'

'Amazing.'

'Not bad is it. What I want to do next is rig up a table-lamp. I've got this chianti flask at home and all I need is the proper attachment. They might make a fuss about curtains, but I'm bringing some sheets back the next time I go on leave. I know it's the army, but one might as well be comfortable.'

I read Stanford's poems that night. They were romantic and gloomy with many references to time and coffee cups and forlorn meetings on railway platforms. He wrote like a man who had experienced the anguish of lost love, but when I asked him who it was he was writing about he hesitated before answering. 'Just someone I know,' he said eventually.

'Did she give you a bad time?'

'They're not exactly *literal* poems,' he said. 'I mean they didn't actually *happen*.'

'But they're about someone.'

'In a way,' said Stanford. 'Me mostly. They describe a frame of mind.'

'I see,' I said doubtfully.

'There *is* a girl,' he went on. 'But I've made her into a fiction. In the poems she's a symbol of all that's impossible, all that I want but can't have.'

'What's her name?'

'Margaret,' said Stanford. 'But I call her Katherine.'

'Why?'

'Because I'm not writing about the real her.'

'I see,' I said again.

Stanford shook his head. 'No you don't.' He held up two short stories which I had brought to show him along with my poems. They were based on incidents I had reported while covering the courts and stylistically they bore the scars of an intensive reading of Ernest Hemingway. 'You think that only realists understand the truth,' said Stanford. 'All that broken glass and rain in the gutter. But you're wrong. There's more than one side to it.'

He had big watchful eyes and a nose that curved like the blade on a tin-opener. His hair stood on end as if it had been brushed the wrong way and he leaned forward with his head tilted to one side as though he was anxious to catch every word of the conversation.

'You do it your way and I'll do it mine,' I said.

'Writers should exchange ideas. D'you think I'm wrong?'

'Not at all. I just don't want to argue.'

'Why not?' he demanded. 'There's not enough argument around here. You learn by debate. Don't you see that?'

I knew what he meant but by then it had become a minor consideration. What I found irresistible was that I had at last met someone who felt as passionately as I did about writing. For Stanford – as for me – it was not merely a diversion or a hobby, but a way of understanding and explaining the world. It was priestly in its purpose but thrilling too, and anyone who practised it belonged to an extraordinary élite. Writers were spies and explorers and interpreters who could undergo hardship and excess and emerge from the ordeal with something of value. It was a discovery which I wanted to shout aloud and at the same time hug to myself as a source of secret power. I imagined it as an incantation which, if spoken at the critical moment could win a war or flog a weary miler past the finishing line.

All through that long summer we met and discussed the books we had read and the books we would write. We talked about painting and films and photography and Stanford had opinions and information on every topic we touched. I knew more about jazz and dance music than he did. But Stanford's musical taste ran from Artie Shaw to Vaughan Williams. He was the first person I had ever known who kept an advance listing of concerts and talks on the wireless so that the shape of his week was decided not by military matters, but by the timing of a Brahms recital or a lecture on the pronunciation employed by Shakespearian actors at the Globe Theatre. The army became an irrelevance. What mattered lay ahead. We quizzed and catechized each other in a state of constant excitement. We bickered, wrangled and disagreed. But we always managed to stop short of actually quarrelling. I had never known a friendship like it.

I told Stanford about Emma and Sadie. He told me about his home in Surrey where his father, a talented and cantankerous engineer, had walked out of job after job because he felt he was undervalued. He remembered his toys being sold to buy food and hiding under the kitchen table with his mother to avoid the rent collector.

'Why don't you write about that?' I asked enviously.

'I can't. Not yet.'

'Why not?'

'Both my parents are still alive. I don't want to hurt their feelings.'

'But it happened to you as well as them.'

'They'd be upset. They wouldn't understand.'

'Pity.'

'I won't forget about it,' said Stanford. 'It all happened. It won't go away.'

Obviously not, I thought. I understood why his poems were about a re-invented girl and why he found my kind of reality intolerable. All the same, I imagined the stories his experiences could make and I regretted the waste.

*   *   *

Stanford's posting to the Army Education Corps came through when I was in hospital suffering from an abcessed ear. I fainted one day when I was cleaning out grease traps in a yard outside the cookhouse and came to on a bare cot in casualty where my temperature was found to be 103 degrees. An orderly poured peroxide into my ear instead of olive oil and when I screamed at the pain I was put to bed and examined by the doctor.

'Do you often get earache?' he enquired.

'This isn't earache.'

'What is it then?'

I tried to explain while my head throbbed and boomed and the ceiling seemed to drop like a steam-press, holding me captive while the flesh baked on my bones.

'You're making a lot of fuss,' said the doctor.

I told him about the peroxide and he raised an eyebrow. 'That was careless.'

'It's like acid,' I said. 'I can feel it burning a hole.'

He peered into my ear and smiled reassuringly. 'There's just a little inflammation.'

'What about my temperature?'

'We'll soon bring that down.'

'Thank you sir,' I said, but I was not convinced.

At the end of the week I was sent to see a specialist near Oxford and for the next few months I travelled between camp and hospital, while the few army friends I had made were picked off, one by one, to join drafts to Singapore and Bremen and Milan. Stanford, who had desperately wanted to travel, wound up only a few miles away at Bulford in Wiltshire. He wrote long letters on sheets torn from army notebooks. Poems interspersed his news and when I told him that I was keeping a file of all his correspondence he replied immediately to say that he bloody well hoped I was. 'Everything is for the record,' he reminded me. 'Whoever dies first has to write a biography of the other. And I plan to be the first to go.'

In time my ear healed and the specialist pronounced me fit for light duties. I went home on seven days leave, hitching a lift by lorry to Tamworth and from there by private car to Stoke. The driver was a commercial traveller for a pottery firm.

'That was my dad's job,' I told him. 'He worked for Macintyre.'

'When was that?'

'Years ago. He died when I was four.'

He glanced at my uniform. 'That's going on a bit. There've been a few changes since then. It's all austerity now. Not like it was in your dad's day.'

When he dropped me near the station he tucked a pound note into my pocket. 'Go on, take it,' he said when I protested. 'I know what it's like being a bit short.'

I made the mistake of telling my mother about the gift. 'He must have thought you were on the scrounge,' she said.

'No he didn't. He was just being decent.'

She pursed her lips. 'It's still wrong to take money like that.'

'It would have been rude not to.'

'We won't argue,' she said.

'A friend of mine says we only learn by argument.'

'He's wrong,' said my mother. 'He's talking through his hat.'

In fact, we argued less than we had done for years. My being in the army set in abeyance most of our usual disagreements. It was as if, in my mother's eyes, my uniform conferred an authority which she had never previously acknowledged. When I changed into civilian clothes before going out she seemed disappointed. 'I want them to see you looking like a soldier,' she said.

'I'm not a real one. The war's over.'

'That's beside the point.'

'Not to me it isn't.'

'I don't mean I want you fighting,' said my mother. 'It's not your fault. You're still doing your bit.'

Apart from Arthur Jolley I was the youngest of the

old avenue gang and most of my childhood friends had seen active service during the last eighteen months of the war. I realised how galling it must have been for my mother to have been shown photographs of my contemporaries in their battle-dress and not to have been able to join in the game by producing similar pictures of me. 'I've got no medal ribbons,' I warned her.

'That doesn't matter.'

'All right then. Just this once.' I changed back into my uniform and made the rounds of our neighbours.

'They've all had a good look,' I reported.

'Did you see Mrs Witcomb?'

'And Mrs Cook. And Mrs Pointon. They all know I'm in the army now.'

'That's good.' My mother folded her hands in her lap and leaned back on the settee. It was a pose in which I most often remembered her; the light from the garden striking the silver blaze in her hair, the birds on the shed roof busy behind her profile. But suddenly she looked older and I was reminded how many people were saying that the war had exhausted them, although all they had done was stay at home and watch it from afar. It was as though the war had fed on their courage and their anxiety, mopping it up like gravy from a plate.

'I shall be getting my posting soon,' I said.

'Where do you think they'll send you?'

'Germany maybe. The Middle East.'

'Let's hope it's somewhere interesting,' said my mother. 'It's a great opportunity, really. We never had the chance to travel like that.'

'It won't be a Cook's Tour.'

'I don't suppose it will. But they look after you. You can't say they don't.'

My mother was deeply impressed by the efficiency of an organisation which supplied clothing, food and transport on such a vast scale and saw it as largesse provided by the state, in return for no more than simple duty. 'They get it all wrong sometimes,' I said.

My mother looked disbelieving. 'I'm sure they know what they're doing.'

I thought of convoys arriving in camp in pitch darkness with no one expecting them and no one admitting that they were in charge. 'Not always,' I said. 'You have to look out for yourself.'

'That's just initiative.'

'I expect you're right.'

'You don't have to agree,' she said. 'I don't have to be humoured.'

She had decided to forgive me for my defection at Christmas, but I still felt reluctant to mention Sadie. I had no doubt that my mother regarded her and London itself as rival attractions and I wanted no bitterness before I went away. My mother, however, chose to surprise me. 'How's that girl of yours?' she asked.

'She's all right, thank you.'

'Do you see much of her?'

'How can I? I don't get much leave.'

'Is it serious?'

I shrugged slowly. 'I don't know. It could be. We decided against getting engaged. There's no point really.'

'You're very young,' she said.

I thought of Emma and Alice and the commitments about which my mother knew nothing. 'Not that young.'

'Too young to tie yourself down.' She stared through the window into the small garden where the lupins had gone to seed and the phlox hung like tattered flags. 'She can come and see me, if you like. If she means something to you, we ought to find out how we're likely to get on.'

'I'll tell her what you say.'

'Let her make up her own mind,' said my mother sharply. 'Don't try and tell her what to do. Just tell her she's welcome.'

At breakfast the next morning I broached the subject to Mary. 'What's going on?' I asked. 'Who's my mother been talking to?'

Mary juggled an array of bacon off-cuts under the grill and slid two slices of bread into the pool of fat beneath them. 'She's talked to me. And your Uncle Ernest. You upset her at Christmas. She didn't know what to do.'

'I know,' I said. 'I'm sorry.'

'She thought you might stay away for good. She didn't want that.'

I watched her tip the bacon on to the bread and then fry two eggs in the remaining space. It looked a very tidy arrangement. 'I'd never stay away for good. How could I?'

Mary looked at me sideways. 'I reckon you could manage.'

'Never,' I said. But I knew she was right.

'Anyway,' said Mary. 'We told her she should make an effort. Be a bit more agreeable. People ought to look each other over before they make up their minds. That way they see what they're getting.' She took two plates from the heating rack and served our breakfast. 'It cuts both ways,' she said. 'I reckon that girl of yours might be in for a bit of a shock. I wouldn't fancy meeting your mother for the first time.'

'You're a crafty old devil.'

'You're not the only one with brains,' said Mary. She cut her fried bread into equal squares and dipped one of them into the heart of the egg. 'God knows what they've been feeding these chickens on,' she said. 'I've seen bigger yolks in frog-spawn.'

I enjoyed my leave. For the first time in years I was not under attack. The night before I left, my mother ironed my shirt while Mary hovered to one side, afraid that she might drop the flat iron.

'The last time she tried this, it fell on her foot,' she said.

My mother tossed her head. 'Don't tell tales.'

The iron cruised over my shirt and there was a faint smell of burning. 'You'll be sending him off with a singe on his b.t.m,' said Mary.

'No I won't.' My mother finished her ironing with a flourish and draped the shirt over the fireguard to air. 'There you are,' she said. 'I'm not such an old crock.'

I put my arm round her. 'It's lovely.'

When I wore it next day the shirt smelled, not of scorching, but lavender. 'I sprinkled a few drops on,' said my mother. 'It's from the bottle you gave me.'

It had been my Christmas present, but although the thought was fresh in both our minds neither of us referred to it. I could still smell the lavender when I got back to camp that night and I slept with the shirt under my pillow.

The following week I was posted to Leicester on a refresher course for shorthand and typing. Casey Warren came with me, so did Sims and Dollimore. We were billeted in a grimy terraced house in a street behind the station, five of us in an attic bedroom which sprawled beneath the eaves with a single light bulb dangling from the rafters. Our landlady was named Mrs Connors. She was a large, blowsy Irishwoman with a beehive of bright yellow hair and a tubercular husband who sat hunched over the kitchen fire, spitting moodily on to the coals. There were also three daughters who worked in a hosiery factory. On Saturday nights the entire family went out drinking and their going to bed was signalled by the sound of Mrs Connors urinating loudly and at length in a galvanised bucket she kept at her bedside.

The first time we heard it we were too astonished to respond. But when the ritual was repeated, night after night, we would wait until it was under way, then applaud as if we were being treated to an aria, a command performance for our ears alone. Sims, in particular, was fascinated by the capacity of Mrs Connors' bladder. He began to time each deluge and at its conclusion, shout his estimate to the floor below.

'Two minutes, Mrs Connors!'

'You dirty young buggers,' she would bellow back. 'I'll be up there in a minute.'

'Three minutes, Mrs Connors!'

'To hell with all of you. You're just jealous of me kidneys.'

She ruled her household with love and violence. Her daughters, although they engaged us in saucy backchat and squealed when they passed us on the stairs, always managed to squirm out of reach when words seemed likely to be followed by action. And her husband, Daniel, frequently displayed a black eye or a split lip, the result of some marital dispute which Mrs Connors had settled in the best way she knew how. He had not worked for five years. 'He's a poor creature,' she told us. 'His lungs is like tissue. One good puff and they'd come apart.'

When she was in a good mood she would make him a bowl of beef tea and feed him like a child, spooning limp crusts into his mouth and dabbing at the drips with a duster. She treated him like a pet, fond when he kept to heel but terrifying in her rage when, as frequently happened, he rifled her handbag and made off to the pub with the housekeeping money. One evening she hauled him from the public bar where he was about to pay for a round of drinks and dragged him the length of the street by the collar of his jacket. It looked as though bloody murder was going to be done. But as he passed us, his feet trailing in the gutter, he gave us a sly smile and winked. 'Her bark's worse than her bite,' he assured us later. 'When it comes down to it, she knows who's boss.'

Each day we travelled by bus or army lorry to the nearby suburb of Hinckley where we attended classes at the technical college. It was like being back at school and the girls we met at the local dances seemed younger than anyone I had known in London. Most of them worked in the garment industry. They holidayed at Butlins and showed us photographs of themselves posed against fountains shaped like pagodas or ice-cream cones. They adhered to a strict code of sexual conduct. When we took them home from dances there was a session by the back gate which lasted no longer than five minutes. They kissed, but never with an open mouth and although they allowed their breasts to be stroked, contact with bare flesh was forbidden. They expected to be married by the time they were eighteen and anyone who was still an old maid at twenty was thought to be odd.

We also went to dances at the De Montfort Hall and once when Casey Warren and I went to hear the Ted Heath band our happiness was made complete by meeting Johnny Gray, the saxophone player, in the gents. He had a large handlebar moustache and he was out of temper because someone had smudged his shirt front with cigarette ash. As a fellow musician, Casey took it as an affront to his profession. 'A marvellous musician like that,' he complained. 'Coming to the sticks just to get his shirt front dirty.'

When the course ended it felt like the end of term. We gave a party for the staff and everyone promised to write. It had taken the army approximately a year to teach me skills which I already had, but the time had not been wasted. I realised, to my surprise, that I had enjoyed myself. By putting on a uniform I had shed responsibility. It was like acquiring a parent or a guardian for whom one did not have to pretend affection, but whose equally impersonal patronage took care of the essentials. It did not suit everyone. David Williams had escaped back to his mum. But when I thought of Peter Stanford and the niche which he had devised for himself I saw how fruitful the relationship could be. Survival did not depend, as Harry Barnes insisted, on not caring. What one had to do was merge with the background and adapt.

We returned to Cirencester for a week, then entrained for the transit camp at Thetford. It was bitterly cold and we slept with layers of newspapers between our blankets. The army seemed to own all of Norfolk. Snow fell and the roads were choked with columns of bren-gun carriers, tanks and lorries. Even the slush was khaki. We were sent on embarkation leave twice and I was put on a charge for losing one of my mess tins. For six days I did cookhouse fatigues and on the seventh I was handed a whitewash pail and told to paint the top layer of coal in the fuel depot where it faced the road.

'Smarten the place up,' said the orderly sergeant. 'Make it look soldierly.'

We were placed on draft to the Middle East the next day. That night I crept round to the back of the fuel depot and kicked down the bank of coal I had so carefully painted. As we drove out of camp, bulky with small-packs and ammunition pouches we would never use, I saw the long hill of whitewash shattered like an egg-shell. Instead of making my mark, I had erased it. My relationship with the army had been restored.

Six

MADAME STENKA, our landlady in Cairo, had a portly brown spaniel which took its exercise on the flat roof of the pension, ambling between avenues of flower pots and peeing on dwarf palm trees, trays of courgettes and tubs of morning glory with a fine impartiality.

One morning Bob Dawbarn, my colleague on the army magazine *Parade* which employed us both as writers, appeared at breakfast with a large gash on his chin. 'There I was having a peaceful shave,' he said, 'when a dog flew past the window.'

The apparition was explained when the spaniel's corpse was found four storeys below. But even before the body was discovered the strangeness of the incident seemed to us in no way exceptional. Cairo was an altogether strange city. That winter the first snow to fall in Egypt for thirty years feathered down from a dark sky and men and women ran into the streets with their tongues out to catch the drifting flakes. At the same time we decided that we had a spy in the pension, a mystery woman who wore glasses so dark and opaque that her eyes were completely hidden and who could be heard making impassioned telephone calls in an unknown language soon after the weekly meeting of British personnel in the sitting room.

Nothing we discussed had any military importance. The army had been withdrawn to the Canal Zone several months previously and the few soldiers who remained all had civilian jobs and dressed accordingly. There was a small contingent of military police whose main task was to keep a look out for British deserters working their way to the coast where they hoped to hitch a ride home.

107

But there was no work for a spy. We debated whether we should lay false trails in our talks to give her something to report. But it seemed too complicated and no one wanted to get the mystery woman into trouble.

Parade was a weekly magazine which was styled on the British *Picture Post*. It circulated throughout the Middle East and had a writing staff of four with a civilian photographer named Colouris, whose main income came from advertising and a range of pornographic portfolios, which he printed in the unit darkroom. He was an excellent technician and lavished the same skills on genitalia as he did on his portraits of the Sphinx at sunset. He catered for all tastes, failing to please only once when he produced a set of anatomical studies, rich in gynaecological detail, and spread them over the lunch table for our consideration. Bob looked at them carefully, then turned them face down. 'It's like looking at chopped liver,' he observed.

Bob was a bombardier in the Royal Artillery, but his rank was a perk that went with his job on the magazine, and seeing him in his civilian disarray it was unnerving to imagine what he would make of a uniform. He was short and bandy with a straw-coloured moustache and a curiously angled body which distorted any jacket or sweater he managed to borrow, so that long after he relinquished it the garment still retained his shape. Fresh from the laundry, his shirts looked unironed and when he reached across the table to refill his glass he shed buttons from neck to navel. He had worked as a reporter on a local paper in Ealing, but on *Parade* he flourished as the caption writer in charge of pin-up pictures, sent to us in batches by the War Office in London.

We called his department the Crumpet Bureau. The pin-ups, usually of starlets in one-piece bathing costumes, were chosen by someone who imagined them tacked to locker-room doors by lonely soldiers and, almost invariably, they looked both winsome and resigned. The girls had been told to be sexy, but in a nice way. They were ambitious and they were being obliging. And it showed.

Bob laboured to make them more interesting, but his imagination flagged until he turned up one set of pictures which featured a skimpily clad blonde disporting herself on an airfield. She was photographed in cockpits and on wing-tips, swinging propellors and pulling away chocks until every RAF duty had been cannibalized in the name of cheesecake. Bob arranged them to make a story-line, then typed his opening caption. I looked over his shoulder and read the first sentence: 'There are fairies at the bottom of my aerodrome....'

It was a new beginning. The starlets became Amazons, district nurses with secret ambitions, physicists working their way through college. Bob was liberated. He abandoned facts, apart from the vital statistics which accompanied each pin-up like a prison number, and gave his girls new and intriguing identities. He was even moved to apply his imagination to other parts of the magazine, starting with the letters page which was starved of correspondence. Each week we padded it with letters of our own in the hope of starting a controversy, but our readers remained unresponsive until Bob supplied a short entry which began 'No one can possibly doubt that the earth is flat.'

It was as though he had touched a button buried somewhere between Alexandria and Trieste. The shock waves rolled onwards and outwards. Letters flooded in, not only from the lunatic fringe but from ostensibly sane and rational men whose faith had either been shaken or stirred by Bob's pronouncement. After six months we declared the correspondence closed. Bob was content. 'I don't suppose we proved anything,' he said. 'But it's nice to know there are so many nutters about.'

He drew comfort from the thought that eccentricity ran like a secret stream beneath the rock of army routine, but I suspected that most of the mail was a reaction to the boredom induced by sun, flies and sand – the unchanging constituents of the Middle East. I was familiar with all three. When I first arrived in Egypt I had been sent with the rest of my draft to Fayid, the army base on the shores of the Great Bitter Lakes. They were linked, we were told, to the Red Sea and the water was so heavily impregnated with salt that it was impossible to sink. On the far side of the lakes lay the desert, 'the blue' as veterans called it, where British and German tanks, burned and gutted in the battles of only a few years ago awaited the salvage contractors from Cairo to pick them apart for scrap.

I worked as a clerk, typing out letters and requisition forms and endlessly snipping out War Office amendments to paste into Standing Orders. We spent our mornings and evenings in the office and had the afternoons, when temperatures reached their peak, to ourselves. Usually we swam in the Bitter Lakes, paddling out to rafts moored half a mile from the shore, where we basted ourselves with coconut oil and lay in the sun until we were giddy. Our tans deepened and darkened, but there was no one to admire them. In all of Fayid there were around three thousand troops and perhaps forty women, mostly ATS, who were rarely seen outside the offices or the officers' club. The camp was kept clean and partly policed by German prisoners-of-war. We shared guard duties and I became friendly with a corporal named Koenig who had served in the Afrika Corps and whose wife and two sons had died in the fire bombing of Dresden. None of them knew when they were likely to be repatriated.

'To me it hardly matters,' said Koenig. 'But some of the men have families. It is not just. The war is over. They want to go home.'

'Were you a Nazi?' I asked.

He bared his white teeth as if he found the question amusing. 'Was I a party member? No. Did I support Hitler? Naturally. I was very young, younger than you. I did what everyone did.'

'Would you do the same again?'

'Probably.' He stared at the bleached-out sky in which

kites circled, spying out the rubbish dump. 'If there was a chance of winning. Not if I thought I was going to end up here.'

It was Koenig who arranged the visit of a truck-load of prostitutes to the German lines every Saturday night. Negotiations were conducted in the back room of a novelty shop in the Arab village by the Sweetwater Canal. Payment was always demanded in advance and the money was earned by the sale of cigarette cases, lighters made from old cartridge cases and greetings cards, painted with schlosses and country cottages. The army turned a blind eye to the Saturday night visits. They were managed discreetly and, it was thought, reduced tension among the POWs. But one night Koenig's body was found on the wire surrounding the camp. His throat had been cut and his pockets were empty. There was an enquiry, but no arrests.

'It was the wogs,' said one of Koenig's friends. 'They wanted more money. Now who will bring us the women?'

In the store where we bought paperbacks and American magazines I discovered Olympia Press editions of D.H. Lawrence and Henry Miller and lay on my bed reading them while the wind snapped the canvas of the tent and dust devils spun like tops between the guy ropes. Dollimore, who had travelled on the same draft and had the bed next to mine, was a connoisseur of dirty books. Lawrence, he argued, was too literary ('Bloody stupid, all that hanging flowers round his cock.') But, like me, he admired *Tropic of Cancer* and had committed his favourite passages to memory.

' "She sniffed out her pleasure on the high hills and in telephone boxes," ' he intoned. 'Bloody good, that.'

' "Hope is the enemy," ' I replied. 'That's even better.'

Dollimore wagged a reproving finger. 'Don't kid me. You don't read a juicy book for bits like that. What you want is something to cheer you up. You don't want to be made more miserable.'

I agreed about the dirty bits. I found them cheering

too. But what most excited me about both books was that they were written with utter contempt for censorship. Reading them was like gulping down raw oxygen. I felt that I was being addressed directly and that the message was coming through without the fuzz of static or the bleeps of good taste.

'I'd like to write like that,' I said.

'They'd lock you up.'

'They've never locked up Henry Miller.'

'He's American,' said Dollimore. 'They're all bloody gangsters over there. They're not going to worry about a dirty book.'

I got out my notebooks and revised several of the stories I had written at Cirencester. In the afternoons the offices were deserted and I sat beneath a fan which barely stirred the air, typing in solitude, happier than I had been for months. I sent two stories to *Selected Writing* and, much later, received them back with a letter from the editor, Reginald Moore, regretting that the magazine had closed down but with a postscript which said 'your writing is above the average.' I wanted to show it to everyone, but wrote to Peter Stanford instead. We had remained in touch since our respective postings and his letters, spiky with comment and patterned with poems, arrived like instalments in a dialogue unaffected by time and distance.

I valued the letters but I missed Stanford's company. It was frustrating not to be able to invoke his instant reaction or try out a new idea or challenge his dawning sophistication with a lurid account of some sexual adventure. I got on well enough with Sims and Dollimore and the others in the tent but, apart from the army itself, we had little in common. Passing a hut on the outskirts of the camp one afternoon I heard piano music and following the sound, discovered a slight figure in a sports shirt sitting to one side of a large radiogram. He waited until the record came to an end, then inclined his head. 'D'you like Nat Cole?'

'Very much.'

'How about this one?' He put on *Sweet Lorraine* and again we sat without speaking until the end of the record. He did not snap his fingers or beat time with his foot, but there was no mistaking his enjoyment. He seemed to soak up the music, slumped in his chair and remaining absolutely still as though any unnecessary movement would interrupt the process of absorption. He had curly brown hair and a pleasant lumpy face. His expression was mild but sceptical. He would be hard to impress, I thought.

'Are they your records?' I asked.

'Some of them. I've just started the Fayid Jazz Club.' He shrugged deprecatingly. 'It's something to do.'

His name was Frank Burdge and he came from North London. His last job, he told me, had been in engineering, but his ambitions lay elsewhere. He showed me an account he had written of working as a lather boy in a barber's shop at the Angel. 'But what I want to do most is paint,' he said. 'I'm trying for art college when I get out of this lot. There's no reason why I shouldn't get a grant. Other people do.' He did not sound entirely convinced. People from his background were not in the habit of being given grants and he knew it. 'But I'll give it a whirl,' he said. 'They can only say no.'

The Jazz Club attracted around twenty regulars. We shuttered the doors and windows and, in the artificial gloom, listened to Sarah Vaughan, Count Basie and Stan Kenton. Frank's musical tastes were progressive; more so than mine. He never propagandized and none of his enthusiasms were voiced with Stanford's dogmatism, but he had a cool authority which carried me with him. He detested the music that was played through the loudspeakers at the roller-skating rink in the camp shopping centre. But, out of what seemed to me, sheer perversity, he spent two or three nights a week there, lounging against the zinc-topped bar drinking rum and Coke while selections from *Oklahoma!* and *Annie Get Your Gun* boomed over the Tannoy.

'How can you stand it?' I demanded.

Frank looked around him at the clusters of ATS girls outnumbered by their escorts, at the trinket sellers with their trays piled high with sun-glasses and junk jewellery and at the skaters, floating for a moment like moths beneath the arc lights before disappearing into the darkness that was Africa. 'I like it,' he said. 'It's different.'

Dollimore was another patron of the rink. Like us he was still a private, but he seemed to have unlimited funds and bought us round after round of drinks, paying for them from a roll of notes which he stuffed carelessly back into his pocket without checking the change. 'How come you're so loaded?' asked Frank.

Dollimore tapped his nose with his index finger. 'Ask no questions, hear no lies.'

'Flogging stores,' I suggested. There was a thriving black market in army equipment which we all knew about, but Dollimore was a clerk with no access to the goods which were in demand.

'Not stores.' He smiled foxily and raised his glass. He had forsaken rum and Coke for Stella, the local beer, and the mixture was having its effect.

We led him away from the rink and waited while he was sick by the side of the path. Behind us the arc lights still burned, punching a hole out of the night. The music had changed to a rhumba and the skaters staggered in their rhythm as though an enormous magnet was tugging at their wheels through the concrete. 'By Christ,' said Dollimore. 'I've had a skin-full.'

His pocket flap was unbuttoned and as he reared up on his knees the money fell to the ground. I picked it up and counted it. There was over thirty pounds. 'Where's it from?' I asked.

'Wouldn't you like to know.'

'Tell us,' said Frank. 'We won't let on.'

Dollimore thought about getting up, but decided to remain where he was. 'Private enterprise,' he said. 'Dead secret.'

He did not tell us that night, but eventually we learned where the money came from. Dollimore was attached to the Pay Corps whose presiding genius at Fayid was a sergeant who had invented a phantom army of Arab labourers. Each week their wages were drawn and shared out between all those who performed the necessary paper work. The accounting was destroyed as soon as the money had been distributed.

'But won't someone find out?' I asked.

Dollimore sighed. 'Won't you ever learn about the army?'

I remembered Stanford and the recreation room which he had made his home for months on end and I understood what Dollimore meant. Any document or diversion could be buried in a bureaucracy which was so vast and so sure of its own efficiency. 'You're going to be rich,' I said.

Dollimore inspected the creases in his newly laundered shorts and scratched away a frosting of starch. 'I shouldn't think so. It's nice to have the gelt, but I'm not really in it for that. It's like your mate and his jazz club. It's something to do.'

My posting to *Parade* came through unexpectedly. I had been urged to put in for it by Bob Dawbarn who was passing through the camp on his way from one assignment to another and who introduced himself at one of the jazz club meetings. 'There's a vacancy coming up next week,' he said. 'There's no one else in line for it and you could get in first.'

'Would I stand a chance?'

'Certainly you would.'

I studied the ramshackle figure beside me and realised that whatever qualities were required, smartness was not among them. 'Would you put in a word for me?'

'For what it's worth.' Bob drew fiercely on his dog-end and his moustache sizzled. 'Just whack in the application,' he said. 'I'll tell them you're bloody marvellous.'

Whatever the reason, my application succeeded. I was told to deposit my kit in stores and issued with a sports jacket and two pairs of civilian slacks. 'You'll be able to buy the rest in Cairo,' said the quartermaster. 'Poncey shirts and that. I'm told they've got an arrangement with some geezer. Cut price for all poofters.'

The arrangement was with Mr Jacobs who ran a small store off Kasr El Aini, close to the pension and on the way to the office. He offered us drinks and cigarettes while I looked through his stock and when the pile of shirts and underclothes that I was persuaded I would need stood taller than the till, he suggested that I should open an account. 'Pay when you like,' he said. 'No interest. Special price for the British army.'

He entered my name in a ledger and made a parcel of my purchases. It was growing dark by the time we left and as he waved us goodbye from the open doorway an assistant fitted shutters of steel mesh over the windows. It seemed an unnecessary precaution in such a quiet district.

'It's not always so quiet,' said Bob. 'They burned a tram outside the pension last week and they've got it in for Jacobs. Naturally.'

I did not understand him. 'Why "naturally"? Who are "they"?'

Bob took my elbow and steered me under a street lamp. 'Two points to get clear,' he said. 'Jacobs is a Jew and the wogs hate all Jews. They want them out, just as they want us out. We're not popular. "They" are the nationalists. At present they support Farouk, but he can't hang on much longer. He's screwing himself stupid and we keep hearing about a revolution on the way. Let's hope they put it off for a few months.'

Walking to the office next morning we were stopped by a crowd that had gathered outside the police station. Some one had been arrested in a street demonstration and there were fears that he had been beaten up. I was pressed against the wall of the building and found myself looking down the barrel of a police carbine. It was choked with dirt and I wondered who would be hurt most if it was fired. The crowd was composed entirely of young

men, most of them students. They carried placards
printed in Arabic, but punctuating their chants was the
name of Farouk and the hatred with which it was uttered
was understandable in any language.

We managed to squeeze our way into a side street.
Someone spat in my face as we broke through the crowd
but as I turned to see who it was Bob hurried me on.
'Don't push your luck,' he murmured.

'Is it always like this?'

'No. They only put on a show every week or so. Most
of the time there's no trouble.'

At the office all was peaceful. We occupied an entire
floor in a block of flats in the garden suburb, and the
rear windows looked over a well of green in which fountains tinkled and a man in a white gallabeiya crawled
over a small lawn clipping the grass with a pair of shears.
Bob called out to him and lowered a filing tray on a
length of string. The man saluted and filled the tray with
flowers. Bob threw down five cigarettes and hauled the
tray back through the window. 'He's the gardener,' he
explained. 'The place belongs to some millionaire. He's
not going to miss a few daisies.'

I met the rest of the staff. The editor was a small,
nervous Yorkshireman named Mac Race who blinked
continuously and wore a Fair Isle sweater. There were
two senior writers, Les Barrett from Tyneside and Stanley
Maxton, who had just caused convulsions in HQ by disappearing into Palestine for six weeks where he had lived
in a kibbutz while, close by, British soldiers were dying
in ambushes organised by the Irgun Zvai Leumi. The
inquest on his extended assignment was still going on,
but Maxton was unperturbed. He blew clouds of pipe
smoke towards the fan and smiled peaceably. 'You've
got a good story and I'm OK,' he said. 'What's the
problem?'

Mac Race waved away the pipe smoke. 'Nobody knew
where you were. That's the problem. You could have

been killed for all we knew.'

'I wasn't. As you can see.'

'He's a big lad,' said Les Barrett, who was tall and dark, and already drinking his first beer of the day. 'He can take care of himself.'

Maxton was a Scot who yearned to live and work in the Middle East. He had fair hair and a neat moustache which had been bleached by the sun. He was soon to be demobilized and was trying to arrange his discharge in Egypt where he hoped to establish himself as a local correspondent.

'You don't suppose this'll help things,' said Mac.

'I don't see why not.'

Les Barrett looked reproachfully at his empty glass. 'The army moves in a mysterious way,' he said. 'Trust in the powers that be and ye shall be disappointed.'

Les was in charge of production. The magazine was printed in Cairo and although the plant was modern and reasonably efficient, there were difficulties with Arab proof readers who understood little English which necessitated considerable resetting. 'I'm not bothered,' he said. 'I'll be done with all this soon. In six months' time I'll be drinking a proper glass of ale instead of this piss.'

We ate most of our meals at the pension, but we had an office cook named George who was Sudanese and had three wives. George thought he was over sixty although he was not certain as to the date of his birth. His wives were considerably younger. 'Maybe nineteen, twenty,' he said when we asked him. 'Old wives no good.'

'How d'you manage?' asked Bob.

'Manage?'

'How do you manage to keep them happy? One man, three women.' Bob mimed fatigue by slumping forward in his chair. 'Very hard work.'

George untied a small pouch that hung from his belt and loosened the draw-string. '*Kif*,' he said. 'Makes a man strong.'

He rolled a slim cigarette between his fingers and we

shared it between us, sucking in the smoke with noisy draughts of air. I felt the veins in my temples expand and I could see time flowing ahead of me like a broad, unhurried stream. All sense of urgency dissolved in the current and I wondered how George found the energy to attend to one, let alone three of his wives.

The office secretary was Edmee Cohen. She had a mane of black hair and when she combed it she threw back her head so that her throat was bared as if it was being offered to the executioner's knife. It was more than a fanciful notion. Edmee believed that the revolution was on its way. 'When it comes,' she said, 'there will be no more Jews.' For years her ambition had been to marry a British officer who would take her away from Cairo, away from Egypt. She saw herself at home in Wimbledon or Scunthorpe, places she had heard of, but could not envisage.

'Tell me what they are like,' she demanded. 'Would I be happy there?'

'They're not like Cairo,' I said. 'You'd hate the cold. It rains a lot and there's rationing.'

'Who cares about that?'

'You would,' said Bob. 'You're not used to it.'

Edmee shook back her hair and her throat shone like a column of ivory. 'I would suffer anything to leave this place.'

She believed that she was being sincere. But by temperament and upbringing she was a true Cairene and it was difficult to see her in any other setting. She belonged to a sailing club. She went to the races at Gezira. Bob and I took her to Groppi's where she ate dish after dish of ice-cream and summoned the waiters by clapping her hands, ordering them to clear the table and bring fresh glasses of iced water while she gloated over the array of cakes on the trolley at her elbow. She came with us to the cinema and we took her home by gharry, cramming ourselves into the pungent cab with portholes on either side and kissing her in turn until the driver grumbled over his shoulder and Edmee pushed us away and sat erect, her hands folded in her lap. 'He's Muslim,' she hissed. 'He doesn't approve.' The disapproval frightened her, but she despised it too. 'They're barbarians,' she said. 'They're a thousand years out of date.'

When Mac and Stanley Maxton went to the wedding of one of George's many nephews she listened, tight-lipped, as they described the ceremony. The bride and groom had withdrawn into a room, they told us, while a chorus of older women wailed outside the door. After half an hour the groom had emerged, waving a blood-stained sheet. 'Disgusting,' said Edmee. 'And they think they can run a country.'

We were all aware that change was on the way. There were more demonstrations. Another tram was burned outside the pension and Madame Stenka, who had fled Czechoslovakia with her husband in 1938, stood at the window and watched the coils of smoke eddy and drift towards the Blue Mosque. She was looking for someone to buy her establishment, but after a year of advertising there were still no takers. Mr Copeland, a lecturer at the university who rented a double room on the first floor, had his classes halved and several of his private pupils – elegant young men who joined us for coffee to practise their English – suddenly decided that they had no further need of tuition. 'It's very hurtful,' said Mr Copeland, 'I feel that I've failed them.'

He was an elderly bachelor who wore silk suits the colour of lemonade and a monocle which he screwed into his good eye while the other wept as though a concealed pipe had sprung a leak beneath the parchment of his cheek. He dabbed at it with a handkerchief which, between times, he kept tucked in his jacket sleeve. He had lived in Cairo for over forty years and had planned to end his days there. He was not resentful about what was happening, but puzzled. 'Where else could I go?' he asked. He had a sister in Basingstoke, but they had never been close. She disapproved of his attachment to the young men he taught, and wrote to say that she could not see him settling in Hampshire. 'She regards me as a foreigner,' he said, toying with the notion in the same abstracted way that he fingered a string of amber beads looped around his watch fob.

Parade, we thought, might survive for another six months before the War Office closed it down and replaced it with their own house magazine, *Soldier*. 'Make the most of it,' advised Stan Maxton. 'The peace is closing in. *Après* us, the deluge.' We re-wrote agency stories, I devised a film feature, hard reporting dwindled to nothing. Most evenings we drank in a bar which, before the war, had catered principally for the crews of ships using the Suez Canal. The proprietor was Greek and he too was preparing to go. At the end of the evening he always bought a round of drinks, but gradually his hospitality increased until every third round was on the house. 'Drink up,' he urged us, 'what else am I going to do with it?' He foresaw a Muslim régime in which all alcohol was banned and his licence would be revoked. In a rare moment of optimism he had ordered a batch of advertising cards and, glass in hand, he recited the text which was printed in English and French on one side, with a street map on the other. 'Ships may pass in the night,' he intoned. 'But, in Cairo, pilots of the world meet at the Little Bar. It has all you look for. Come and feel that you have selected an intimate bar.' He handed each of us a card as a souvenir and then, with brimming eyes, dumped the rest of them in the waste bin.

One night the police raided the pension. There was an inspector and six constables with guns. None of them spoke English but Mr Copeland, who appeared wearing a scarlet robe with a cowl, interpreted fluently and advised us to gather in the sitting room where Madame Stenka would bring us coffee. 'They say they are looking for a dissident,' he reported.

The mystery woman screwed a cigarette into a long black holder and accepted a light from the inspector. 'Why do they think they will find him here?'

'Someone told them.'

'Provocateur,' she growled and the tip of her cigarette burned cherry red.

Although it was three in the morning she still wore her dark glasses. Madame Stenka's hair was netted, as if to protect it from hungry birds, and her husband, I noticed, carried a cane, as though he was planning to take his constitutional walk the minute that the search party left.

'Does this happen often?' I asked.

Mr Copeland dabbed at his eye. 'Frequently. They vary the time, but this is the hour they prefer.'

'Have they arrested anyone?'

'Not so far.'

'They wish to unsettle us,' said the mystery woman. 'It is a war of nerves. They want to drive us out.'

The search took half an hour, at the end of which the lieutenant apologised for disturbing us, saluted and ordered his squad down the stairs. The coffee left me wide awake and after staring at the ceiling for an hour I went up onto the roof to watch the dawn. It was accompanied by the sound of radios being switched on all over Cairo. All of them were playing music; not the same tune, but with the same reedy core and a beat which shuffled and skipped beneath the melody. The muzzeins joined in, their calls to prayer amplified like station announcements, and beneath an exhausted yellow sky the faithful turned to Mecca. I could not see them, but the city seemed to stir audibly and scratch itself. As the sun rose the kites began to gather. They were the same scavengers which had picked over the rubbish of Elizabethan London. The army called them 'shite-hawks' but they were handsome birds, soaring on thermals and planing over the dun coloured houses and office blocks on broad wings. In the distance I could see the fuzzy geometry of the Pyramids, their building block silhouettes already blurred by dust and heat. In one sense it was an exciting place to be. There was an atmosphere of intrigue and impending violence. Revolution hung in the air like electricity before a storm. But it offered no involvement. The cause was not ours; we were detested by everyone concerned. The mystery woman was right.

They wanted to drive us out and I was ready to go.

When the order came from London to bury *Parade* we gave an office party which lasted for twelve hours. The bath was packed with ice and then filled with bottles. George prepared a buffet meal and, as the guests arrived, sat in a corner weeping happily and smoking *kif*. Colouris invited his favourite model, who climbed on to a desk in the centre of the room and performed a belly dance. We watched her muscles squirm like snakes from her pelvis to her diaphragm and then make the return journey. 'It's funny,' said Bob. 'I quite fancied her till I remembered those photographs.'

We took Edmee for a farewell dinner at Shepheards, but it was not a success. She flinched when the waiter served the meal as though she already saw him in another role, leading the mob which would drag her from her apartment. 'You don't believe me,' she said, 'but it will happen.'

Her arm was pebbled with cold and I stroked it in a forlorn attempt to comfort her. 'Of course it won't.'

'You don't know. And you won't be here to find out.'

We rode home by gharry, but the only time we kissed was when we said goodnight. 'You mean goodbye,' said Edmee.

'We'll keep in touch.'

She shook her head. 'Oh no, you won't. No one ever writes and, anyway, what's the use?'

We watched her enter the apartment block and the door close behind her. The gharry driver clicked his tongue and the horse ambled on its way. 'She'll be all right,' said Bob.

'Of course she will.'

'Will you write to her?'

'I expect so. How about you?'

'There's not much point. She said so herself.'

Our gharry paused by the Abdin Palace and when we looked out the sentries at the gate snapped to attention. It was a game we had often played before, but it no longer seemed funny. I thought of the fat king, consoling himself with his women and his collection of glass eyes and the loot he had consigned to his Swiss bank account and I shivered as Edmee had done in the restaurant. 'What d'you think he's doing up there?' I said, peering at the windows which glowed across the courtyard.

Bob followed my gaze. 'Same as us. Packing his bags.'

We left Cairo the following day. Mac Race stayed behind to perform the last official rites while Les Barrett and Stan Maxton – whose request to be demobilised in Egypt had been refused – sailed for England. It would be Bob's turn soon, but to my delight I had been posted to Athens to work as a feature writer on the army's daily paper, *Union Jack*. It was another winding-down operation but I could think of no better place in which to spend my remaining time in the army.

Greece, for me, was the country described by Henry Miller in *The Colossus of Maroussi*. As the troop ship which took us from Alexandria to Piraeus neared the coast I went up on deck to see the islands emerge from the haze, and the quality of light which Miller had written about so lyrically seemed to silt down, replacing the mist with flecks of crystal which framed boats, rocks and buildings in shining air.

I was billeted in a house at the centre of the town with a fellow writer on the newspaper named Sydney Edwards. He was plump and pale and wore pyjamas with broad red stripes which pointed like a flare path towards the Acropolis when that evening he fell to his knees by the side of his bed and began to pray. I was not prepared for this demonstration of piety, nor for its repetition next morning. Sydney's face was as smooth as lard, but there was no mistaking the intensity of his feelings. I hid behind my pillow until his devotions were concluded, following which he climbed back into bed and after several moments of contemplation, wrote carefully in a notebook which he then tucked under his mattress. It transpired that Sydney was a member of Moral Rearmament and his prayers, he believed, gave him a direct line to God. During his morning meditation the thoughts which came to mind were subjected to tests of Absolute Purity, Absolute Truth and Absolute Honesty. If they passed muster they were held to come from the Almighty and had to be acted on, whatever the consequence.

Sydney and I had travelled together from Egypt and, caught between paydays, I had borrowed £5 from him. I intended to repay the loan at the end of the week, but as we made up our beds on our first morning in Athens he asked for his money back.

'I haven't got it yet,' I said.

'That's a pity.'

'Don't worry,' I told him. 'I won't run away.'

He reminded me every day until payday when I drew on my credits and handed over the cash. He showed no particular satisfaction as he tucked the notes inside his paybook, but I imagined that I saw something flicker behind his spectacles as though in a remote cubicle a till had been rung up and a receipt issued. That afternoon when the billet was deserted I examined the notebook under Sydney's mattress. Just as I had suspected, our transaction was noted down, along with other items of unfinished business. Against my name he had written 'Ask P. for money back. Accept no excuses.' I was distinctly impressed. No one else I knew could consult a divine debt-collector; nor did His assistance end there.

Moral Rearmament was not only a religious organisation. Its political influence was formidable, especially in Greece where the MRA gospel of anti-communism was welcomed by a government which was waging civil war against the Left. The support of MRA whose members included not only the faithful and the famous but also opportunists in military, diplomatic and trades union circles was openly courted, and many prominent Greeks, including members of the cabinet, climbed on to the MRA bandwagon. Once installed they had the ear of whoever they wished to impress with the rightness of their cause, and their availability for interview or consultation was cited by Sydney as proof of democracy in action.

'You wouldn't believe how nice they are,' he told me one afternoon when he had been granted an audience with the Prime Minister.

'They're nice to anyone they want to use.'

Sydney's face stiffened. 'You're just being cynical.'

'Not at all. Think it through. They're selling propaganda and you're happy to buy it.'

Very little of the MRA doctrine appeared in the columns of *Union Jack*. Officially, the British army was neutral in the civil war and our news coverage was meant to reflect our independence. In fact, both the British and American military supported the Greek establishment, whereas the paper veered Leftwards. This was largely due to the News Editor, Mike Priest, who ran *Union Jack* with utter disregard for the edicts of the Editor, Major Tarrant, whose newspaper experience was confined to several years in the advertising department of a large provincial chain.

Major Tarrant had a passion for royalty. Any king or queen whose doings were reported in our pages were, by editorial decree, granted the prefix 'HM'. In a long report this produced an extraordinary effect, rather like a sustained hiccup, and the peppering of capital letters whenever the royal personages made an appearance made typographical nonsense. Major Tarrant, however, stood firm. 'I'm a loyal person,' he declared. 'The world may be going to the bow-wows, but as long as I'm here we shall show respect.' He had no time for emergent nations or pinkoes in government or anything which he saw as a portent of the changing times. When I suggested writing a series on jazz for the Saturday supplement of the paper he agreed, with the proviso that I should concentrate on white musicians. 'We have to keep our end up,' he said. 'For me, the black man begins at Dover.'

Mike Priest offered him no direct challenge. Instead of engineering a confrontation in which there would have to be a winner and a loser, he exploited Major Tarrant's incompetence by pretending that the Major's policy was being followed to the letter and that any deviation was entirely due to his misunderstanding of what was required. The backlog of complaints soon became too tangled to unravel and while the paper continued to appear, promptly and despite extreme technical difficulties, Major Tarrant was reluctant to look too closely into the breaches of discipline which nagged him like flies whose buzz he could hear but never locate.

Major Tarrant slept late and led a busy social life, so that for most of the day Mike was in charge. He spiked stories which he thought were politically unsound. He controlled layout and wrote headlines. He had a good working knowledge of the antique flatbed press on which the paper was printed and if Major Tarrant, emerging from a late lunch flushed with brandy and patriotic fervour, attempted to remake a page he would never argue but simply remind him of edition times and problems with printers until the Major divined what was at stake and bowed to the inevitable. He liked to boast of his Fleet Street connections and assured us that he was a contributor to many of the magazines which were sent to us in a weekly parcel from London. His name, however, never appeared in a by-line. 'No mystery about that,' he said, lowering one eyelid. 'Can't let the War House know that I'm moonlighting.' He had a broad, handsome face which shone as if it had been varnished and a handlebar moustache whose chestnut horns were rigid with pomade. His hair was parted in the middle and descended to his ears in a series of small corrugations like ripples on a pond which, unaccountably, had frozen as they formed. He reminded me of one of Raglan's troopers riding towards the guns at Balaclava and wondering who was pelting him with cannon balls.

The paper was printed in a converted garage adjacent to the meat market where sides of lamb, carcases of kid and poultry, tied together like feather dusters, hung beneath naphtha lamps. We went to press at nine-thirty. The first copies were inspected to ensure that the paper was damp enough to absorb the ink, then we adjourned to one of the pavement cafés to drink ouzo which curdled in the glass like Jeyes fluid when water was added. There was a hushed roar from the lamps as if breath was being exhaled in concert and along the avenues of meat the young men of Athens strolled, hand in hand. Sometimes we went to the Missolonghi Club which advertised dancing and cabaret, but whose entertainment chiefly comprised shuffling between the tables with one of the hostesses to music from a vintage radiogram. The girls were of all nationalities. The German and Italian armies had occupied Athens, so had the British and American and they had all brought their camp followers. There were frequent arrests to check up on papers and permits, but the most important document was a certificate of health, renewed weekly, which promised that on the day of inspection the holder was free from venereal disease.

It was not a guarantee of safe conduct. Billy Hunt, one of our compositors, had contracted syphilis twice, despite reporting faithfully to the Prophylactic Station for morning-after treatment. He now preached total continence and tried to discourage lechery in others by describing the pain he had suffered from massive injections of penicillin. 'It was agony,' he declared. 'If you want proof you can take a look at my arse. It's like a dartboard.'

When it grew too late to expect any more customers the girls would gather at our table for a final drink. Several of them wore what looked like ivory crosses around their necks, but they were carved from sheep's bone to which grime and body sweat gave an instant patina. They were made by a shepherd who visited Athens once a month to claim his stock and replace it with another batch for seasoning. The girls were paid a small fee and the crosses were sold as antiques. One of them, we were told, was believed to have cured a woman of infertility.

'That's not the sort of miracle we want here,' said

Maria, who had worn it. 'We're not in the baby business.'

She was a stocky blonde with a shading of dark moustache. Her parents, she said, had starved to death during the German occupation and she would often point with pride to the range of hills overlooking Athens on which partisans had painted the single word 'OXI' – a defiant 'NO' in letters thirty feet high – to remind the occupying troops that resistance was not at an end. With six or seven other girls she shared a large apartment close to Ommonia Square. It was not a brothel, although the visitor was expected to make a cash donation, however brief his visit, and there was a housekeeper who charged overnight guests for their food and a change of sheets. There were several bedrooms, none of them luxurious; a sitting room full of chairs upholstered in Liberty chintz and a kitchen with a wood-burning stove and a canary in a wicker cage. Its plumage was the same shade of yellow as the floor tiles and when it sang, the cups on the dresser shivered in their saucers. There was no paper on Sunday, so we had Saturdays off and, like the girls, we slept late. We ate breakfast at noon. There was bread and honey, and coffee in two aluminium pots, one at each end of the table. The girls arrived in relays, smelling mustily of bed and squinting through eyes still clogged with mascara. Most of them were pale and plump and their thighs and forearms had the look of pastry dented by busy fingers.

Sometimes we borrowed the unit jeep and drove to the coast for a picnic. The rocks were red and the sea a deep blue. We bought wine and cheese and plates of small fried fish from a taverna and fed each other until we could eat no more. It was like being adopted by a family. We showed each other snapshots. We oiled each other's backs. We played beach games and practised tricky dives from each other's shoulders. But there was always an end to play. By the time we drove back to Athens a line had been drawn between recreation and paying customers and for the next six days we kept our distance while business went on as usual.

*   *   *

As spring warmed into summer the city took on a new look. Houses were scrubbed and the woodwork brushed with paraffin to prise out bugs and other insects. Sallow walls were whitewashed. The orange trees lining the streets burst into flower and nightingales sang in the Zappeon Gardens. Behind our billet the neighbour's pig circled its pen, sniffing the poached ground for scraps of food and rasping its flanks against the stuccoed walls. At night its sigh of relief drifted into our room like the murmurs of a well-fed ghost.

It had been a hard winter. The war had gone on for too long and the casualty lists included the names of brothers and lovers, lost or buried in the mountains. Convoys of wounded arrived in the suburbs around nightfall or in the early morning and drove to the military hospital only when the streets were empty and there was no one to see. The communists, said the Government, would soon be defeated; but there was no appetite for victory. It was not a popular war. The communists had fought the Germans and too many people in the present administration were believed to have been collaborators. Issues were not clear cut. Feelings were exhausted and there was a tendency to laugh or cry rather than to reason.

It was at this juncture that the saints made their appearance. Most of our reporting in Athens was limited to covering government briefings or events organised by the British Council, while the ordinary life of the city went unnoticed. But one morning a young secretary named Ionna Hatzigiannis glanced at a first floor window of the Greek Air Ministry and saw, to her surprise, the figure of the Virgin and Child. We heard about it half an hour later when a crowd gathered and blocked the road, so that Air Ministry officials, innocent of the cause of the disturbance, locked all doors and readied themselves with rifles and grenades to deal with a full-scale riot.

'Bloody oiks,' said Major Tarrant.

'You mean the Air Ministry?' said Mike Priest.

'Don't be obtuse,' said Major Tarrant. 'The crowds. Those Johnny Greeks. What do they think they're up to?'

I went to find out. By the time I arrived the police were already clearing the street and the window was being cleaned under the supervision of men in uniform. One of them sat on the sill picking his nose while the window-cleaner, braced on a rickety ladder, polished the pane with a chamois leather. As the window dried the figures reappeared. They looked like oil streaks on a wet road, but the shapes and colours remained constant. I saw the outline of a blue robe on the larger figure and a patch of red where the face might logically be situated. The Child was less clear but to one side there was a blob of yellow, as though a light bulb was being shone through the glass.

My photographer squinted through his viewfinder and pressed the button. 'It's a bloody halo,' he said .

The crowd would not go away, but ten minutes later it moved on when a second vision, almost identical to the first, was seen in the window of an advertising agency three streets away. By noon over twenty visions, covering the scale of divinities, had been reported.

'It's an illusion,' said Major Tarrant. 'They're all pissed. We're going to ignore it.'

'I saw something,' I said. 'I'm not saying it was a vision. But there was something in that window.'

'Did you get a picture?'

'In process.'

Major Tarrant distended his nostrils as if he was trying to release something which had stayed up there by mistake. 'We'll see then. We'll bloody well see.'

But the picture proved nothing. There was a vague outline as I remembered, but in the photograph it looked like a smear on the glass and, in black and white, the illusion of flesh and garments was missing.

Major Tarrant studied it through a magnifier. 'There's bugger all there.'

I pointed to where the infant head seemed to rest in the crook of the arm, but he was not persuaded. 'These bloody Greeks,' he said. 'They think they can pull a fast one. Well, they can't fool me.'

'Nobody's trying to fool anyone,' said Mike Priest. 'It's just a happening. All we have to do is report it.'

'We don't have to report anything.'

Mike sighed. 'Just as you say, sir. Your decision.' He turned to go, but lingered at the door. 'Mind you,' he said, 'they'll all be talking about it at the Grand Bretagne. Wondering what's going on. Asking what the facts are.'

'They can bloody well find out for themselves.' Major Tarrant pushed the photograph to one side and straightened his desk in a show of efficiency, but his confidence was shaken. The Grand Bretagne was where he met his fellow officers and ladies from the British Council over cocktails and it was essential to be up on the latest gossip. 'Put someone on to it if you like,' he said carelessly. 'I'm not making an issue of it. I just don't want you to think I'm buying a lot of Johnny Greek nonsense.'

Mike Priest nodded again. 'Just as you say, sir,'

He made Sydney Edwards our Godspotter. 'It's an honorary title,' he said. 'But we think you have the connections.'

Sydney was not amused, but he was thorough. He pinned a street map of the city to the wall and our office became an Incident Room where each new sighting was logged. The Virgin and Child were given a red pin, the Virgin alone, a blue pin and lesser dieties made do with white. 'What does the MRA think about it?' I asked. 'What's the party line?'

He consulted his notebook and stuck another pin on the map. 'It's nothing to make jokes about. We have no criteria.'

'How about the Three Absolutes?'

'They don't apply.'

'Too bloody true,' said Mike Priest. 'Maybe we should bring in a witch doctor.'

By the end of the second day we had more than fifty visions pin-pointed on the map and the story was getting out of hand. The saints had appeared in the windows of liquor stores, one-night hotels, army billets and private houses. Districts were beginning to compete with each other. No neighbourhood wanted to be without its saint. Vigils were kept on street corners where the most notable manifestations had occurred and in the suburbs of Kallithea a girl of fourteen was said to have exhibited signs of the stigmata.

Sydney wrinkled his nose. 'That's disgusting.'

'What is?'

'People bleeding,' said Sydney. 'It's unpleasant.'

He was genuinely offended. But what upset him even more was that no one seemed able to provide a rational explanation for what was happening. One lobby argued that the city's water supply had been polluted and the images on the windows were made by traces of some chemical agent. There were suggestions of mass hysteria, while another group proposed that the saints were the advance guard of a second coming which would bring the civil war to an end.

Major Tarrant sniffed out the political implications. 'Pretty bolshy lot, these saints,' he declared.

'How's that, sir?'

'Wanting peace at any price. Isn't that the ticket?'

'People are fed up with fighting,' I said. 'They want it to stop.'

Major Tarrant stroked his moustache as if it fed him with intelligence denied to the rest of us. 'Wheels within wheels,' he said. 'Tactics you wot not of.' He slapped the top of his desk, signalling an instant decision. 'We're dropping the story. Not another line about these Johnny Greek saints. Take no notice and they'll go away.'

He was almost right. After four days in which Athens had turned itself into a revivalist centre, the Church and Government formed a united front and decided to ignore the saints as if they were uninvited guests at a party who could be shamed into leaving. No new sightings were officially recognised although several were rumoured. Crowds were dispersed, not with the usual rough handling, but with a tough geniality which jollied along the spectator and lessened the upset. The visions disappeared from the windows in which they had taken up residence, melting into the glass as if whatever stabilised them had been diluted by weather or a growing indifference so that their presence was no longer justified.

'Something was there,' I said. 'I saw it.'

'You saw what you wanted to,' said Major Tarrant. 'Not that it really matters. I suppose we all made a few ackers from it. I certainly did.' His big, polished face shone like an ornament and I imagined him dusting it every morning before he put on his uniform. 'You'll be going home soon,' he said. 'Better get used to earning the honest penny again.'

The following month we celebrated Easter. We cracked eggs which had been dyed scarlet with the guards at the Evzone barracks and the one whose shell remained unbroken longest was promised good luck for the rest of the year. Standing between the columns of the Acropolis that night I watched a long procession of worshippers, each of them carrying a lighted candle, thread their way through Athens and climb the hill to the monastery of Lycabbetus. The tiny flames puckered in the wind, but the chain was unbroken. I went back to the office and turned out our photographs of the saints. None of them looked remotely as I had remembered them. The body shapes were blurred. The smears on the glass meant nothing.

'Don't worry about it,' advised Mike Priest, working late as usual. 'We weren't trying to prove anything.'

'I suppose not.'

'Of course we weren't,' said Mike. 'They cheered people up. They were useful at the time. That's all you need to believe.'

I remembered what he had said a week later when we sailed from Piraeus. The sun was up and, beyond the jumble of the waterfront, the squares and palaces

and temples stood in their compounds of light. On the
hills overlooking the city I could see the partisans' slogan
– the white-painted OXI – quivering through the haze.
And below me along the quayside drove a convoy of
ambulances carrying wounded from the war in the
mountains.

Seven

I LAY on the floor of the bedroom in Chelsea and listened to George Melly snoring. It was six o'clock in the morning and no one else was awake. George had the best bed because it was George's room. Two other bodies were clasped together on the cot next to it. The rest of us, curled on mattresses and huddled beneath overcoats, were there because it had been late when we left the London Jazz Club (the band had played a dozen choruses of *Get Out of Here* before the basement emptied), and later still when we straggled from the café opposite the Windmill Theatre. The last tube had long gone and there was a grille like a portcullis barring the entrance to Piccadilly Underground.

We were all slightly drunk. In the café we had met a prostitute named Jean who told us she was in love with a girl who had travelled south with her from Glasgow. 'I take care of her,' she said. 'She's only a wee thing. I won't have her round here where the others can lay their dirty hands on her. They're all thieves. They don't care about other people's feelings.'

'I care,' I said.

'Like hell you do,' said Jean. 'None of you bloody care and why should you?' She lit a cigarette and squinted at us through the smoke. Suddenly she began to cry but no one attempted to console her. Like students gathered around a hospital bed we watched huge tears roll down her cheeks to form twin pools on the table top. Our interest was clinical. We had no desire to interrupt the experiment. 'All my life I've wanted to give a tart a baby,' she said.

'I know how you feel,' said George. 'I've always wanted to have one.'

Quite possibly it was true I thought. Earlier that year George had arrived from Liverpool wearing a tight blue suit, his face blotched with gentian violet. He had impetigo, he explained, but he thought the colour of the ointment quite flattering. He also suffered from a barber's rash which glowed hotly above the collar of his shirt. His hair had been cropped at the back so that a plume of oily bristles stood up from the crown of his head and his lips were wet, red and negroid. Habitually, he wore in his buttonhole a pink celluloid doll with its buttocks uppermost, and carried a walking stick whose ivory handle was carved into a tableau at the centre of which there crouched a plump and terrified mouse. It seemed to have been petrified the moment before being seized by the talons of a hawk and I thought it both beautiful and repellent.

George was an anarchist and a surrealist. Also, he let it be known, he was homosexual although he showed more than a passing interest in women. He had a job as the assistant curator of an art gallery where he gave readings from the works of Kurt Schwitters, ending each poem with the prescribed smashing of wine glasses. On two or three evenings a week he sang with Mick Mulligan's Magnolia Jazz Band, shouting traditional blues into a biscuit tin (perfect, he said, for amplification) and spent much of his free time listening to the records of Bessie Smith whose angry bellow we all fervently admired. It was not only that she was Empress of the Blues. She was also black and, consequently, oppressed which made her the perfect icon for our group.

We longed for revolution, although what form it should take we did not know. The London Jazz Club had an anarchist bookstall where the best-selling pamphlet was Henry Miller's *Murder the Murderer*. I still owned the Olympia Press edition of *Tropic of Cancer*, the first dirty book I had encountered which could pass as literature. And we suffered Miller's polemics in the hope that somehow sex had been smuggled into his sermon.

We were disappointed. There was better value, said

George, in *The Lay of Maldoror* a prose poem by the Comte de Lautréamont. But although we listened respectfully while he recited his favourite passages it was hard to share his enthusiasm. It was easier to respond to the pictures he praised: collages in which tram tickets and scraps of photographs overlapped, and etchings by Max Ernst in which leaves, rocks and the heads of birds were stamped on the page like fossil remains of the living world. They were not only great art he told us, but good investments. Few of us had the money to act on his advice. But he persuaded Mick Mulligan, richer than most of us in his capacity as the Director of a wine and spirits firm, to buy a Max Ernst folio.

It was not entirely what Mick had expected. To him 'art' was a word with sexual connotations. It meant horny painters and willing models and a generally licentious view of the world. Judged by these standards, Max Ernst did not come up to scratch. 'Thanks very much, cock,' he said as George showed him the plates which made up *Histoire Naturelle*, 'but there's not much tit, is there.'

George's own collection was more comprehensive. When his grandmother died, leaving him several thousand pounds, he spent the lot on pictures. He too acquired a Max Ernst folio, but in his Chelsea digs pride of place was given to two paintings by René Magritte. They hung on the wall facing his bed, and lying among the jumble of bodies in the pale morning light I felt, not for the first time, that I was inside an envelope, air-mailed from some exotic land. The pictures surrounding me were the stamps. One seemed to be the portrait of a woman, although on closer inspection I could see that her features were made up of breasts, navel and a tuft of pubic hair. It was called *Le Viol*. The other, in which mysterious objects like bedsteads floated in a green sky was called *Le Drapeau Noir*.

I shifted my position on the floor and viewed them from another angle. It was Sunday morning and no one was likely to be stirring for several hours. George's landlord was an amiable and tolerant writer named Bill

Meadmore. He and his wife put up with the stream of unannounced dossers drawn by the haven of George's front room, but when the traffic was heavy – as it invariably was at weekends – it was wiser to make use of the bathroom and lavatory before they felt their territorial rights threatened. When that point was reached Meadmore was likely to make a dramatic appearance and indicate with a finger vibrating with suppressed rage that it was time to go.

There were other good reasons for making an early start. On Sundays George insisted that everyone sharing his room helped to clean it and the task could only be avoided by sneaking out before the sleepers awoke. It was a poor way to repay hospitality but I enjoyed walking through the empty streets to the station to catch the first train to Ealing where I had my own digs with Bob Dawbarn.

Bob had been at school with Mick Mulligan at Merchant Taylor's and he was now the trombonist with the Mulligan band. It was one of several occupations he had tried since leaving the army. His old paper had refused him a job and when I called him the day I got back to London he had just returned from his early morning shift as a milkman. I introduced him to Eric Sly and he was now working with me for Sly's agency.

We lived at home with his parents but Bob had a mistress named Thea whose flat was only three streets away. She was fifteen or twenty years older than he was; a small, slender woman with hennaed hair and veins which stood out on her wrists like twigs beneath the skin. She had a high, breathless voice and a repertoire of intimacies such as drinking from Bob's cup or tweaking the cigarette from between his lips which made plain their relationship.

On the walls of her sitting room there were framed prints of girls in slips and camiknickers, posing in puddles of silk, pointing with cigarette holders, all declaring their naughtiness as if it were contraband. Thea's favourite was one called 'Brown Sugar'. She had a bright red mouth and her thighs were banded by black stocking tops.

'A bit like me,' Thea would say hopefully, hitching up her skirt and pirouetting round the settee. She did, in fact, have good legs but admiring them too openly was dangerous. Thea's skittishness increased in direct proportion to the interest shown but she would suddenly switch it off and hop into Bob's lap as if taking refuge from a flood of unbridled lust.

Occasionally she gave parties for which most of the drink was supplied by Mulligan. He had become Managing Director of the family firm suddenly and tragically when his father and elder brother were killed in an air crash. His interest in the business was minimal, but it had its uses. Free liquor was an obvious advantage. But he also used branches of the firm throughout London as temporary billets for out-of-work musicians. The appointments were usually disastrous, but Mick had learned to shelve his philanthropy the moment that profits went into a serious decline. Managers who drank the takings as well as the stock were bad news. And Mick knew when to fire as well as hire.

He had an on-and-off relationship with Thea's daughter, a tall and statuesque showgirl named Gaye who posed nightly in a West End revue with bare breasts and a sequinned turban. The rules of the Lord Chamberlain ordained that nudes on stage should not move and Gaye obeyed instructions to the letter. In fact, she had embraced immobility as a way of life. Her face was flawless and blank. She slept late and spent long afternoons wrapped in a terrycloth robe, stroking her nails with an emery board. She ate absent-mindedly, poking fingers of toast between her plump lips as if they were to be absorbed, not chewed, while cups of tea grew cold at her elbow.

Her reactions were uncommonly slow. Waiting one night for the last tube she walked to the end of the platform at Piccadilly, her hands clasped behind her back. Feeling something placed in one hand, she turned incuriously to see a man in a raincoat with his flies unzipped and his penis resting limply across her open palm. 'All he said,' she told us later, 'was "Do you mind?" It took so long to register, there wasn't time to scream.'

Gaye often said that she and Mick were engaged, but the understanding was entirely in her imagination. Like the rest of us, but without any of our dissembling, Mulligan's pursuit of women was frankly sexual. He had money and a car, but his success was largely due to his goatish good looks and the single-mindedness of his approach. He was dedicated to sex. Nothing was so interesting or, he realised, so evanescent. He mourned every missed opportunity. Even jazz was relegated to second place, although it was a close run thing and usually the two were compatible. Every jazz club audience had its quota of scrubbers – friendly, promiscuous girls whose aim in life was to give aid and comfort to all musicians. But, while he made use of their services, Mulligan's appetite extended far beyond them.

For a while he laid siege to a diminutive girl named Barbara who kept us company day and night and sometimes even shared our beds. But she was a companion and no one's concubine. 'The day I get married I want to wear white,' she explained. 'I shall walk up that aisle a virgin.' Mulligan bullied and begged, but Barbara remained adamant. If anything, her determination increased as he grew more insistent. All men, she decided, were after only one thing, but she was saving it for her husband. One night when the band was engaged to play at the Slade School of Art she was introduced with some ceremony to the Principal, Sir William Coldstream. She shook the hand of her host and looked him in the eye. 'I may as well tell you now,' she said firmly. 'I don't fuck.'

It was a world in which I felt at ease, which was just

as well, for the world to which I had thought I would
be returning had reordered itself while I was away. Emma
had qualified as a teacher and planned to move to a
school in one of the new towns which were being built
on the outskirts of London. Alice was living with her,
as she had always intended, and a house went with the
job.

Sadie had left the Carringtons and rented a bed-sitter
at Finsbury Park. During the previous year we had exchanged only a few letters and although neither of us
had declared our relationship at an end there was no
move on either side to revive it. My mother had invited
Sadie to stay, but the occasion had not been a success.
Both of them described it in guarded terms, but there
was little doubt that each had found the other intolerable.

'I'm not saying she's an *unpleasant* girl,' said my
mother, recalling the visit. 'But there's something posi-
tively grating about her voice. And those clothes! It's
as though she's on permanent exhibition.'

'She can't help her figure.'

'There's a great deal of it,' said my mother. 'And she
likes it to be known.'

She had arranged for Mary to take her on a tour of
my aunts and cousins. 'I felt I was there to be inspected,'
said Sadie. 'I had to show I was good enough to join
your precious family.'

'It wasn't my idea.'

'You could have warned me,' she said. 'You must have
known it was likely to happen.'

I had to admit that she was right. I had guessed that
my mother would put her through her paces. But no
amount of rehearsal would have prepared her for the
scrutiny of my Aunt Ada or breakfast conversations with
Mary over grilled bacon and oatcakes during which confi-
dences were offered in exchange for unimportant returns.
My mother's family and friends formed an intelligence
network which pieced together things heard and things
seen, compiling a portrait which although it was not
an exact likeness, stuck in the mind as stubbornly as

a cartoon. Features were sharpened, defects exaggerated. The verdict was in before the summing-up.

'You knew what they were like,' I said. 'I've told you often enough.'

'Maybe you did, but I didn't think it would be so bad. I kept having to justify myself. They made me feel guilty all the time.'

'Guilty about what?'

'Everything.' She bit her lip in remembered irritation. 'Living in London. Going out. Seeing people. Nothing I did was right.'

'Did they say that?'

'Of course they didn't. It's not what they say. It's how they listen.'

We were on dangerous ground and we both knew it. I could see how Sadie's behaviour would impress my relatives, but I found it peculiar too. Even before I had been posted to Egypt, Sadie had gone out with Harry Barnes. I did my best not to mind, but I could not think of them together without remembering that long exploratory kiss and Sadie's glutted face when he released her. They had continued to meet. 'After all, he's your friend,' said Sadie when it became plain that they were seeing each other regularly and not now and then as she had implied. 'In any case,' she added, 'you've no call to go on about it. We're not engaged.'

'Just as well I should think.'

'You said that; not me.'

We threatened each other without ever making the threat explicit. And each of us used it to justify our independence. I did not tell Sadie about the girls I saw when I was away from her and she left me to imagine who she went out with and what they did when she was away from me. Our letters became formal and false and in Athens I stopped writing altogether.

'You can't blame me that it's gone wrong,' said my mother.

'I don't.'

'All the same, it's probably for the best.'

'It's not over,' I said. 'We've simply not been in touch.'

My mother waved through the window at the shed roof where starlings were stealing the crumbs she had scattered for smaller birds. 'Greedy things,' she said. 'You should tidy things up.'

She did not separate her two complaints, but I knew what she meant. 'It's not that easy.'

'It never is. But you've a chance now to make a fresh start. You don't want getting caught up in a lot of loose ends.'

I had been out of the army for ten days and already I was being urged to come home as though I was a prodigal whose return to the fold had only been postponed by my call-up. I explained as patiently as I could that I had no intention of doing that. But it was no use. Until I left for London my mother would not believe that I was going away yet again.

I told her I had to see Eric about my job. 'He's been keeping it open for me,' I said. 'I have to decide whether I want it.'

'You've already done better.'

'Not here,' I said. 'Nobody knows me here. It'll take time.'

There were perils in discussing journalism with my mother. She had seen signed articles in *Parade* and *Union Jack* and assumed that I was returning to England with an established reputation. 'They don't count for anything,' I told her. 'They were just good practice.' There was even less point in showing her the stories I had written. They were about the army and street life in London and most of them contained scenes and language which made her wince. Watching her turn the pages of a manuscript I could predict the precise moment when she would put it down and take a deep breath as if nerving herself to read on.

'But that's the way people are,' I told her. 'It's how they act and how they speak.'

'There are nicer things to write about.'

'I don't know enough about them.'

'You will,' she said. 'Although you walk in the gutter, look up at the stars.'

I willed myself not to reply. My Uncle Joe who lived in Trenton, New Jersey sent my mother parcels of American magazines, including *Reader's Digest*, whose home-spun wisdom she was inclined to quote without remembering where it came from. Often when I was still seething over some especially sententious anecdote which my mother had told to point a moral, I would find the offending passage underlined in a copy of the *Digest*. The fact that I reacted so sharply was proof that the message was reaching its mark, said my mother. It was the truth which hurt. 'But if you could write like that you'd have something to be proud of,' she said.

I did not show her my poems. They revealed too much of what I felt and I was not prepared to have them judged by the *Reader's Digest* criteria. They were getting better, I thought, but none had yet been accepted for publication. Occasionally an editor would scribble an encouraging note on a rejection slip, but I could only discuss them at length with Peter Stanford and I longed for a more professional opinion.

Meanwhile there was the job to consider. I went to see Eric in his new quarters in a basement beneath the sub-post office in King's Cross Road. The front room looked out on a blank wall and a grating in the pavement. The back room had a badly stained sink in one corner and a ceiling across which leaking pipes had inscribed water marks like the contours on an ordnance survey map. 'We're a lot better off than we were,' said Eric cheerfully.

'I can see that.'

'Mind you,' he said. 'It gets a bit damp in the back. I was going to put a copy typist in there. But there may be a health hazard.'

'That's a pity.'

'People don't seem to have the stamina,' he said. 'I don't know what's wrong with them. I never get ill.'

It was true. Eric's health was aggressively good. He never succumbed to the colds and coughs which laid the rest of us low each winter. Whatever the weather he cycled to the office. He not only worked long hours, but served on several committees whose minutes he invariably typed. His digestion was perfect and he slept soundly. He was an example to us all and resented it.

'We were going to discuss my salary,' I said.

It was the subject which Eric liked least, but he had prepared himself. 'Arthur's back,' he said. 'There's a lot of money going out.'

'There must be more coming in.'

Arthur Sutton, Eric's former partner, had returned to the agency after war service in India and largely due to his efforts business, I estimated, had doubled. 'Expenses are heavy,' said Eric. 'You can't imagine what everything costs.'

'Yes I can,' I said. 'It's the same for everyone.'

Eric studied me over the top of his glasses. 'I couldn't offer you more than five.'

'Five ten,' I said.

He scratched himself briskly. 'That's over the NUJ rate.'

'Only just.'

'All right,' said Eric. 'That's for a five day week. Another thirty shillings if you work on Saturdays.'

We shook hands on it. Eric was a scrupulously fair employer, but he liked to give the impression that somewhere in the negotiations he had scored a point. Possibly, I thought, his advantage lay in my acceptance of the working conditions. Every surface in the office was covered by a thick film of dust which silted down from the pavement and through the grating. The light bulbs were furry with grime and when I trailed my hand across the top of the desk my fingers looked as though they had fondled an ink pad.

'It's a problem,' said Eric. 'In a way it's better when it rains. There's less dust then. But then we get flooding in the other room.'

'That's nasty.'

'And fungus,' said Eric. 'All over the walls. I've scraped it off, but it keeps coming back.'

He did not sound particularly worried and I remembered how indifferent he had always been to his surroundings. Dirt and damp and fungus were inconvenient only when they upset other people. 'I expect we'll manage,' I said.

We agreed that I should start work in a week's time and I climbed the dark stairs ('The bulb broke yesterday,' explained Eric) and closed the street door behind me. I had been away for nearly three years but little had changed. I walked past Riceyman's Steps and the baronial façade of Rowton House and caught a bus to Highbury. After the white light of Athens, London looked shabby and untended. There were still static water tanks, their surfaces green with duckweed, on the bomb sites. And the sites themselves had acquired an air of permanence, as if dereliction was here to stay. Riding along Upper Street I saw leaves sprouting on a tree which shrapnel had lopped in half. But it was the only sign of revival. The shopfronts were drab. The windows of several houses were still bandaged with strips of brown paper, and all along the pavement I saw empty sockets where iron railings, wrenched out to help the war drive, had once stood.

When I telephoned Sadie the previous night she had sounded pleasantly surprised and I wondered if reconciliation was in the air. She was between jobs, she said, so we arranged to meet in a pub in Blackstock Road at one o'clock. I was five minutes early but she was already there, sitting at the bar beside a man in a raincoat. He lit her cigarette, nicking the match with his thumbnail, and whispered something in her ear. I heard the familiar whinny of laughter and saw her breasts shake as she threw her head back. There was a new gusto about her as if she had renounced all attempts at refinement and I felt a spasm of envy mixed with regret that she had rarely looked so happy with me.

She saw me in the doorway and beckoned me across

the room. I leaned forward to kiss her but she held out her hand instead. 'Welcome home,' she said. 'This is Gerry.'

He raised his glass, then shook the hand that Sadie released. 'Pleased to meet you.' He had short fair hair and two of his front teeth were crooked. His expression was good humoured but wary and as we studied each other I remembered where I had seen such a face before. I was eleven or twelve years old and boxing for my house at the Bluecoat school. My opponent had watched me in just the same way from behind the cushions of his gloves before suddenly uncorking a combination punch which knocked me to the canvas. I was counted out and was still groggy when I was helped from the ring.

'What are you drinking?' asked Gerry.

'Bitter,' I said. 'No, Guinness.' I felt out of breath and out of temper. Something was going on which I did not understand.

'Have you got yourself fixed up?' asked Sadie. 'Are you going back to the agency?'

'Next week.'

'Have you found somewhere to live?'

'Not yet.'

'It's not easy,' she said. 'The rents they're asking are terrible. What is it you want? A flat or a bedsit?'

I sipped my drink through the crust of foam. 'I'm not sure yet. I may stay with friends.'

'Best to take your time,' said Gerry. 'Don't rush into anything. Look around a bit before you decide.'

'I intend to.'

He nodded as though he was ticking off an answer in a questionnaire. 'Will it be around these parts?'

'I shouldn't think so.'

'There's nothing going round here,' said Sadie. 'We know. We've been looking long enough.'

I did not respond and the conversation changed gear. We talked about the army and whether or not the prefabs they were building would stand up to the English climate and after five or ten minutes Gerry emptied his glass and said he had to go. He shook my hand again and showed his chipped teeth in a smile. 'Nice to meet you at last. I've heard a lot about you.'

'How's that?'

'You know Sadie. She likes talking about her past.'

'I didn't know she had one.'

Gerry punched my shoulder, lightly but hard enough for me to take notice. 'Everybody has. Not that it matters. Unless you want it to.' He pecked Sadie on the cheek and then, as if one act had inspired the other, kissed her on the lips. 'See you later,' he said, and was gone.

I ordered more drinks and stared at the counter. 'I wanted you to meet him,' said Sadie. 'We're getting married.'

I should not have been surprised, but for a while I could not believe what she had said. 'How long have you known him?'

'Six months or so.'

'Has he met Harry Barnes?'

'No he hasn't.'

'You should arrange it,' I said. 'He ought to know all the old runners.'

Sadie shook her head slowly. 'I don't know why you're angry. You know it was over between us.'

'You didn't say.'

'There was no need.'

'There was for me.' I succumbed to a wave of self pity. 'How was I to know what was going on? I was in the bloody army, miles away. D'you think I'm telepathic?'

She put her hand on mine and squeezed it briefly. 'You're being a dog in the manger. You never wanted to get married. I've met someone who does.'

The fact that Sadie was right did nothing to improve my temper. 'What does he do?' I asked.

'He's in the meat business.'

'You mean he's a butcher?'

'Sort of.' She hesitated, then plunged on. 'He's a slaughterer. Part time.'

I choked on my Guinness. 'Say that again.'

'You heard,' said Sadie. 'You needn't be sneery about it. There's nothing so marvellous about what you do.'

'I never said there was. I'm just envious. There'll be lots of free meals. Lamb chops. Rump steak. Liver and lights.' A list of prime cuts and offal began to form in my mind and I waited until the rhythms were sufficiently firm for me to chant it like a playground rhyme. It was in a playground that Sadie and I had first met. I had hit her with a snowball. We had kissed in the cloakroom. We had made love. We had sustained each other with plans and promises and it was all about to end in disappointment and spite.

'Just shut up,' she said. 'Don't say another word. You don't know anything about him or what he does. I love him and that's enough.'

She was not quite shouting, but her voice cut through the buzz of conversation and I was aware of a growing hush surrounding us like oil on rough water. We were set apart. People were looking at us. The landlord craned over the bar. 'Everything all right?' he asked Sadie. 'He's not giving you any trouble, is he?'

She shook her head. 'No trouble.'

'We're just having a discussion,' I said.

'Are you now.' The landlord nodded towards my glass. 'Drink up and push off. We don't like seeing our regulars upset.'

'She's just told you, there's no trouble.'

He picked up my glass and emptied it in the sink. 'On your bike.'

'You may as well,' said Sadie. 'Or we'll have a row.'

'Just as you like.' I was not carrying it off very well, I thought, but there was nothing else I could do. Everyone in the bar was watching me. 'Nice friends you've got,' I said.

'Gerry's friends.'

'I'm still your friend.'

'For Christ's sake,' said Sadie. 'Can't you leave it alone. There's nothing here for you. Go and find someone else.'

It was like looking at a photograph for the last time before putting a match to it. Once it was done there was no way in which the image could be reclaimed. I did not grieve for what I was losing, only for what we had already lost or abandoned years ago. I saw Sadie's mouth tremble and I remembered it, wet and swollen against my shoulder after making love. I reached out to touch her, but she pulled back and the gesture became a threat.

'All right then,' I said. 'Goodbye. Good luck.'

I paused on the pavement and heard the conversation surge up behind me like foam from a bottle. I jumped on the first bus that came by and found a seat upstairs. We drove up the hill heading west, past the hostel where I stayed when I first came to London, past the road where Sadie had lived with the Carringtons, past the terrace where I had lodged with Minnie and Lily. In my mind's eye I could see envelopes skimming along a conveyor belt and a post mark thumping down on each one of them, cancelling the stamp, forbidding further use.

I travelled to Ealing on the tube. Bob Dawbarn met me at the station and we walked home along a tree-lined road between shafts of primrose sunlight. 'Truly rural,' I said.

'Queen of the bleeding suburbs,' said Bob.

He was as genial and seedy as when I had last seen him and quite unconcerned about the refusal of his old paper to give him his job back. 'There's a chance the band might make it,' he said. 'We've got a couple of bookings this week. There's a rehearsal tonight.'

He limbered up by playing an assortment of 78s on the radiogram in the sitting room, accompanying the bands as the fancy took him. His enthusiasm was unmistakable but his technique was crude. I listened while he imitated solos by Kid Ory and Jack Teagarden, fluffing notes and botching glissandi and I wondered if the rest of the band were any more proficient.

'Not much,' said Bob. 'We're all learning. Anyhow, it's meant to sound a bit rough. That's the point about trad.'

In traditional jazz, he explained, polish was unimportant, even suspect. What mattered most was going back to the roots to find and reproduce the true spirit of the music. When the Magnolias played jazz they felt themselves soul brothers to Bunk Johnson and Louis Armstrong. The blacker they sounded the better. It was a mistake of history and of nature that Bob and Mulligan had attended a British public school, but they were doing their best to atone. Bob put *Muskrat Ramble* on the turntable and eased the slide of his trombone. There was a strangled fart when he tried to blow through the mouthpiece but it was only a fleeting interruption. He turned a tap on the instrument which I had not previously noticed and a blob of what looked like tobacco juice dripped on to the carpet.

'Gunge,' he said succinctly. 'It's murder when it gets choked up.'

'Is it all right now?'

'For a while. It depends on how much I spit.'

We listened to records for half an hour, at the end of which Bob's repertoire was exhausted. He could play the principal solos, copied note for note from the originals, on a few standards including *Careless Love, Willie the Weeper* and *South Rampart Street Parade* and he could busk agreeably on several twelve-bar blues. But his lip was wobbly and his improvisations sounded all the same.

'It'll be all right when we get more practice,' he said.

He was mistaken. The Magnolia Jazz Band rehearsed for three hours that night at Mulligan's home in Park Royal and they sounded worse at the end of the evening than they did at the beginning. 'We'll be all right when we get the bass,' said Bob.

As he had already explained to me they were experimenting with their line-up. For the past month the rhythm section had comprised drums and tuba (which, argued Mulligan, was going back to the great tradition of marching bands). But it had not proved a success. The tuba player had turned out to be phenomenally mean, with a rare ability to make himself scarce the moment that his round was due. It was more than Mulligan could bear and he ended the arrangement without delay. 'Let's face it,' he said, 'even a good tuba player gets on your wick now and then. But a tight-arsed tuba player's worse than Hitler.'

They were now in search of a bass player to replace him. The Lyttleton bassist – a saintly-looking man named Les Rawlings, whose flowing beard and hair cried out for robes to go with it – had sat in with the band occasionally to give Mick an idea of the sound he was seeking. But he had also acquainted him with the problems of transporting a double bass around town. London Transport would not allow the instrument to be taken on either a tube or a bus. There were few cars roomy enough for it to fit inside and it was not considered safe to strap it on the roof. Rawlings told a pitiful tale of watching a fellow musician's bass slide from the luggage rack of the car in front and disappear under the front wheels of the van in which he was travelling. 'It was like running over your granny,' he recalled.

Les was not a full-time musician. He had served as a merchant seaman and held a union card as a sheet metal worker. Playing a double bass, he said, was the hardest job of all. Carting it about created a social problem ('I've never yet had time to pick up a bird after a gig,' he complained) and the fingers of his right hand were permanently encased in sticking plaster to contain the scars and blisters produced by plucking the thick gut.

Mulligan was interested but unsympathetic. He was looking for immediate results and he shied away from more difficulties. Running a band was a dream which he and Bob had shared since schooldays, but he disliked its organisational aspects. What Mulligan wanted was the pleasure of playing and the fringe benefits of sex and company. Bookings, salaries, transport did not interest him. He put up with rehearsals as a necessary chore, but he was glad when they were over.

I wondered – as I had done at Bob's house – how the neighbours put up with the noise. There was no sound-proofing. Rehearsals were held in the sitting room with its leaded lights, its four-bar electric fire and a small bar in the corner. On the facing wall there hung a picture of feasting cardinals, grinning through goblets in some medieval never-never land and on the floor there were stacks of 78s, gritty with dust and ringed by the bottoms of glasses which had rested on them. In the confined space it was difficult to distinguish the melody or decide on tempo. But, beyond the din, what each musician heard was a perfect version of the tune he was trying to reconstruct. The important thing was to try and match the original. I studied Mulligan's purple face, bulging behind the bell of his trumpet and watched the slide of Bob's trombone flash backwards and forwards like a small piston and I envied their absorption. They would go on, not until they got it right, but until they had reached their approximation of what was right. There was a world of difference. 'We're not professionals yet,' Mulligan said crossly when the rehearsal had started fifteen minutes late. He was reproaching himself and the rest of the band. But also, I thought, he was describing a state of happiness.

When the rehearsal finally came to an end he waited until only Bob and I remained. Then he looked at his watch. 'Are we all set?'

'Where for?'

'Eel Pie Island, near Richmond,' said Mick. 'There's a new band playing tonight. Might be worth a listen.'

We drove there in Mick's car. It had only been delivered the previous week and the interior smelled of wool and fresh leather. Mulligan drove with both front windows open, not for ventilation but to give him instant access to girls we passed on the pavement. If he saw a likely prospect ahead he was liable to brake suddenly, stick his head out of the window and ask if they wanted a lift. Although it was getting on for ten o'clock it was not yet dark and even when there were no street lamps we could at least be sure of the sex and approximate age of the girls in view.

Mulligan's enthusiasm, however, led him astray. What he thought was a platinum blonde turned out to be an elderly lady with hair swept back like a hood of stainless steel. Diplomatically, Mick asked her if we were on the right road for the ferry to Eel Pie Island. She told us at some length, suggesting different routes and hazarding how long it would take us to get there. When we drove away she stood on the kerb with her hand raised in farewell as if we were departing guests.

Mick watched her dwindle in the driving mirror. 'How old d'you think she was?'

'Sixty. Sixty-five,' I said.

'Have you ever had anyone as old as that?'

I tried not to sound shocked. 'Not yet.'

'Might be interesting. Did you get a good look at her? Fair old figure. Probably still got her own choppers. You could do worse.'

'I don't know about that,' I said.

Mulligan glanced at me as we drove through an avenue of street lights and I saw the slant of his eyes and the corkscrew of hair that fell on his forehead. 'You should keep an open mind,' he advised. 'You get a lot more fucks that way.'

When we reached the river the ferry was on the far side and Mick flashed his headlights to attract the boatman. Several couples were sitting on benches by the river wall and they huddled closer, shielding each other from the glare. The ferry poled in to shore and we crossed over to the island. The music carried clearly across the water and Bob sang the words to *Oh, Didn't He Ramble*. When we tapped our feet the boat rocked dangerously and the boatman told us to sit still. The island had been a great place in the thirties, said Mick, with bungalows for weekenders and a theatre and several pubs, but the money had run out and most of the properties were now derelict.

He paid the boatman and we walked towards the music. The band was playing in a ballroom behind a large pub. There was a stage at one end with a potted palm on either side and a number of gilt chairs for the band. The piano was out of tune and between each number the pianist lifted the lid and either tightened or slackened a key. Whatever he did had no effect. He had a glass of beer on the piano top and all the band had glasses beneath their chairs. They wore check shirts and cord trousers and only the leader – whose clarinet was patched with sticking plaster and trussed with rubber bands – could read music. They played loudly and cheerfully and I saw the dance floor rise and fall beneath the feet of the dancers like the ferryman's boat on the river outside.

'Solid maple that floor,' said a man standing behind me. 'Twenty thousand springs beneath it. Sprung for dancing. Not for this stuff. Proper ballroom dancing. Waltzes and tangos. They used to hold competitions here. Evening dress and monkey jackets. Very fancy.'

'Why did they stop?'

He watched a girl spin like a top, her skirt lashing her thighs. 'There's no call for it now. I've lived here twenty-five years and I've seen it all. It's not like it was. Girls showing their knickers. Things have changed.'

'Why do you come here then?'

He drank deeply from his glass and stared over its rim at the dance floor. 'It's my local. They're not pushing me out. I've got a right to be here.'

I took my drink on to the balcony. The water sucked at the bank below and threw a trembling pattern of lights back at the ballroom window. There was a smell of soil and cut grass and I could imagine how it had been before the war. Somewhere back in the bushes a bird began to sing, tentatively at first, then with growing assurance as the song took hold. It was not put off by the blare of the band. I felt dew forming like spray on my face and hair and went back inside. Mulligan was talking to the girl who had shown her knickers and when we left half an hour later she came with us in the car.

I was staying the night with Bob, and Mulligan dropped us at the end of the road. 'I'll pick you up tomorrow,' he told Bob. 'Six o'clock sharp. They want us there before seven.'

'Are we getting paid?'

'Only just.' The gig at which the Magnolias were playing was at the Young Zionists in Greenford and the fee was minimal.

'What does that mean?'

'Peanuts,' said Mick. 'Think of it as practice.' He wound up the window, then wound it down again. 'There may be some talent there,' he said. 'You never know your luck.'

He drove off, the girl beside him, and we watched his rear light jerk round the corner like a ruby on the end of a string. 'I'll settle you in,' said Bob. 'Then I'll just look in on Thea.'

'Won't your folks mind you being out?'

Bob looked genuinely puzzled. 'Why should they?'

'Do they know you're with Thea?'

'Of course they do.'

I thought of my own mother and how she would react to my visiting a middle-aged mistress only a few streets away. 'And they don't object?'

'I've told you,' said Bob. 'It's nothing to do with them. So long as we're not at it in the middle of the road why should they worry?'

It was a novel approach to relationships I thought, as I climbed into bed a little later. It saved argument and acrimony. It allowed complete freedom. It went with a new life and a new start. For a moment I thought of Sadie, but what lay ahead was infinitely more exciting. There was no room for regret. I closed my eyes and when I opened them again it was another day.

Eight

BOB'S MOTHER suggested that I should move in permanently the following week. Bob was coming to work for the agency and if we were going to be following the same routine, it made sense for us to be under the same roof.

'The other thing,' said Mrs Dawbarn, closing the kitchen door so that Bob would not hear, 'is you're a good influence.'

'I wouldn't say that.'

She nodded solemnly and the smoke from her cigarette ripened the nicotine stain on her upper lip. 'I love Mick,' she said. 'I always have. But there's no doubt, he leads Bob astray.'

I could hardly explain to Mrs Dawbarn that Mulligan's influence, strong though it might be, was matched only by our enthusiasm for what he proposed. It was more useful, I thought, to reassure her. 'You shouldn't worry,' I said. 'Bob's a good journalist. He'll settle down when he's back at work.'

'You really think so?'

'Absolutely.'

'Bless you,' she said, patting my back and letting fall flecks of ash over the breakfast bacon. Mrs Dawbarn smoked constantly and was never without a cigarette drooping from the corner of her mouth. She had pepper-and-salt hair tied back in a cue and rosy cheeks which had withered like a winter apple. She adored Bob and his younger brother Anthony and fetched and carried for them in a way which my own family would never have tolerated. Her husband had a pink bulldog face and a bluff manner which concealed his chronic uncertainty. He was ill at ease with Bob and Anthony and on guard with an older son and daughter. There was a pretence of consulting him when it was first suggested I should stay there. But the invitation was Mrs Dawbarn's; so was the final decision.

Years before, they had lived in Shropshire and Mrs Dawbarn would sometimes describe their way of life before the war. 'There was always so *much* of everything,' she would say, as if she found it hard to believe the present scarcity. 'I can remember two or three joints of meat in the pantry. Game pies *and* chicken and ham. *And* bowls of cream.' On our behalf she grieved over our pitiful wardrobes and lamented the fact that shirts worn one day had to be washed and ironed overnight to be ready for the following morning. When the trousers of my demob suit split at the knee she shook her fists at the ceiling as if she detected some demon of austerity gloating over my misfortune and offered to advance me the money to buy a new outfit. She was a generous and an impulsive woman and I counted myself lucky that she had made me welcome.

Bob was an instant success at the agency although Eric had been apprehensive on first hearing that he played trombone with a jazz band. 'It's all right,' I told him 'he won't play it here.'

'I didn't suppose he would. It's just that it seems a rather ... rackety occupation.'

'I don't know what you mean.'

'Drink,' said Eric. 'Drugs. That sort of thing.'

'What sort of thing?'

He scratched himself vigorously. 'Late nights. Over indulgence. I can't have anyone who's not up to the mark.'

There was an innocence about Eric which shielded him from absurdity and disillusion. But, as if he suspected his own vulnerability, he sometimes made noises to suggest that he was wise to the ways of the world and that forewarned was forearmed. He was a teetotaller and for reasons both real and imagined he thought drinkers were unreliable. Jazz had connotations which, although

he was uncertain about the details, he knew to be un-
savoury. So, for a host of reasons, Bob gave him cause
for concern.

At the same time, Eric wanted to be fair. 'I'm not saying
anything against him,' he emphasised. 'I'm sure he's capable. I just feel we must know where we stand.'

I said nothing. Given time, Eric talked himself out of
objections. When they had been aired and explained at
some length they usually exhausted themselves, after
which Eric could proceed with an easy mind. While I
had been away the agency had grown. There was more
staff and there were plans to extend the coverage still
further. Arthur Sutton was now in charge at North London. He had decided against reviving his partnership
with Eric ('he worries enough for both of us,' he said),
but as well as reporting, he was there to lend weight
and advice whenever it was needed. He was a testy,
sardonic man who treated the daily proceedings in court
as a passing show from which amusement might be derived and morals drawn. He had a passion for justice
and an equally profound conviction that it was rarely
done. He had served as a major in the army and suspected
that the civilization which he had helped to defend was
not only bogus but corrupt. The thought did not depress
him. Sitting in the press box he rejoiced in the diversity
of fools and knaves who paraded before him in the dock.
He liked to present himself as a staunch conservative
and argued that fellow travellers were traitors to their
country and should be hanged. At the same time he
accepted a commission to write a twelve-part series of
articles for *The British Ally* – an English-language newspaper circulating in Russia – on the British legal system.
He was not being in the least hypocritical in accepting
Moscow gold. 'We might convert a few of the bastards,'
he said.

Arthur had thinning hair and a blue jowl which looked
as though the skin itself had been crayoned. He smoked
a pipe at a jaunty angle and his teeth had grown on
the slant after years of clenching the stem. His shorthand

was meticulous and his reports were both fluent and precise. All that they lacked was the tang of his verbal asides – the anticipatory plea on behalf of someone about to go down for six months on a charge of assault that he was 'a good boy at home,' or the explanation by a receiver of stolen lead that he had bought three tons of the metal in good faith from 'a man he met in a pub.' Arthur was versed in the mythology of petty crime and could invariably sense which legend was about to be invoked and repeat it, word for word, as it was being retailed to the court.

I worked as his deputy for a while ('Just to get your hand in again,' said Eric) but other plans were being laid. Several papers had asked us to supply them with reports from Thames Magistrates' Court – the clearing house for East End villainy – and at first glance it seemed a tempting proposition. There was, as Arthur observed, a lot of crime about, ranging from gang warfare in Limehouse to wholesale larceny from London Docks. But few of the events were being reported.

'Apparently there's someone there,' said Eric. 'But he's not doing his job.' He sounded both disapproving and hopeful, like an entrepreneur who sees opportunities going to waste or an evangelist catching first sight of a pagan province. Eric liked to make a profit, but only when he felt that right was on his side. He believed that natural resources should be developed and that it was his duty to exploit them. There was, as he said, a reporter in residence. But clearly there was more work than he could handle. Diplomacy was called for, but he had no doubt that he could reach an agreement. 'I'll make him an offer,' he said. 'I'm sure he'll be reasonable. He wrote several letters but none were answered. What he proposed was a profit-sharing arrangement which, in time, would become a pension. It was both imaginative and generous, but there was no response. 'Oh dear,' said Eric after a month of silence. 'I'll have to go and see him.' He looked at me speculatively. 'You'd better come too.'

The court was in Arbour Square in Stepney. On two sides, to the north and the east, streets and houses had been erased by bombing. A single telephone kiosk stood among the rubble. Across a wasteland of scorched brick and pulverised mortar I saw a pub marking the end of a terrace of cottages which had disappeared. No bomb had fallen on London for six years, but the sense of devastation was still raw.

The morning list was over by the time we arrived. A group of Sikhs, one with a large sticking plaster strapped across the bridge of his nose, stood arguing on the front steps and a police sergeant shooed them gently along the pavement. 'Go on home,' he advised. 'Take more water with it next time.' He stroked his chin when Eric introduced himself and asked where he might find the court reporter. 'Is he expecting you?'

'Not exactly.'

'Have you met him before?'

'I've written to him,' said Eric. 'But he doesn't reply. It's Mr Clark isn't it?'

The sergeant nodded. 'Old Nobby. What d'you want with him?'

'Business,' said Eric. 'We have matters to discuss.'

The sergeant seemed to be secretly amused. 'Really?' he said. 'That should be interesting.' He pointed across the hall. 'He's still there. Go right on.' He followed us into the court and waited by the door as if reluctant to miss the encounter. 'That's him,' he said nodding towards the press box. 'Go and say hello.'

A small and filthy old man sat huddled in the corner of the press box. He was writing on a block of copy paper, his left arm hooked around the pad as if protecting it from anyone who might want to crib what he had written. His finger nails were long and dirty. His jacket was glazed with grime and the collar of his shirt was stained like a bruise with tide marks of black and yellow. He cocked his head sharply and I saw that his eyes were gummy but bright. Eric put out his hand and smiled. 'Mr Clark?' he said. 'I'm Eric Sly. I've written to you several times. Did you receive the letters?'

Nobby Clark ignored the hand and with a rag, as stiff as canvas, dabbed at the dew-drop that hung from the end of his nose. Dirt was ingrained on his face like a powder burn and when he moved I caught the whiff of unwashed armpits and something worse. It reminded me of meat in high summer and involuntarily I stepped back.

'A bit strong, is it?' said the sergeant behind me. 'It often is. We don't let him get too close to the radiators.'

Eric still stood with his hand extended, but slowly he let it drop as if a train he had been signalling had steamed on in another direction. 'Mr Clark,' he said coaxingly. 'I asked you about the letters. Can we discuss my suggestions?'

Nobby took no notice but dipped his pen into a bottle of blue-black ink and resumed writing. His penmanship was excellent. Over his shoulder I saw lines of copperplate inscribing the page, but when he caught me looking he muttered fiercely and turned the pad face downwards.

Eric leaned forward. 'I'm sorry,' he said. 'I didn't quite hear you.'

'Piss off,' said Nobby Clark.

'I beg your pardon?'

'Piss off,' said Nobby again. Without warning he heaved upwards and launched himself out of the press box, hacking at our shins and clawing at the air as if he was trying to shred an imaginary net. His trousers were as tattered as his jacket and his boots were split and sodden. Every part of him seemed to have been cobbled together and as he shook with rage I seriously wondered if he might come apart.

'Calm down,' said the sergeant. He took hold of Eric's arm and turned him towards the door. 'Best leave it for now,' he said. 'He's a wicked old bugger when he feels like it. Try again later.'

'I don't think there's much point,' said Eric. 'We don't need his co-operation. I was only trying to do what was best for him.' I could see that he was considerably shaken. He had come in good faith to negotiate a business proposition and he had been abused. 'We shall have to make other arrangements,' he said. 'We don't have to put up with this.'

I watched Nobby come to rest. He still quivered like an antique engine whose cylinders fired at random intervals. His fingers still plucked at filaments which only he could see. But slowly his rage subsided. He shuffled back into the press box as if retiring to his kennel and sat down, panting audibly.

'Just you behave yourself,' said the sergeant. 'You'll be getting us a bad name.'

We went with him into the entrance lobby and Eric giggled in his embarrassment. 'Well, well,' he said. 'I really don't know.'

I was accustomed to the mildness of Eric's exclamations, but the sergeant looked disbelieving. 'He's a bit of a nut-case,' he said. 'There was no point in warning you. You have to find out for yourself.'

'Quite,' said Eric. He paused delicately. 'How long has he been like this?'

The sergeant did his sums. 'Years. Ever since his wife died. I knew him before the war. He was all right then. But when the old lady passed on everything changed. He's got a couple of kids. One of them's a solicitor. But they don't want to know. You can't blame them. He's in the dock two or three times a week these days.'

'What for?' I asked.

'Booze,' said the sergeant. 'Drunk and incapable mostly.'

'How can he afford it?'

The sergeant laughed. 'Old Nobby's loaded. He's got a house in Southend and Christ knows how much in the bank. Most nights he kips in a lodging house in Spitalfields. But he could buy us all up if he wanted to.'

'I see,' said Eric.

I could almost hear his mind working. The ethics of

the situation had required him to make Nobby a proposition. But the situation was not what he had imagined it to be. Nobby had no legal entitlement to the job of court reporter. Nor had Eric. Nor had the half dozen other journalists who had established themselves in magistrates' courts all over London. There was an unwritten but generallay accepted law that there should be no poaching on each other's territory. But if the papers who bought reports and paid retainers wanted a change in their representation, there was nothing to prevent it. The sergeant had told us that Nobby was a rich man, so there was no question of stealing his living. Eric considered his position and the evangelist joined hands with the entrepreneur. 'If we move in it's probably for his own good,' he said. 'He shouldn't be living like this. And he's not doing the job properly.'

'He won't like it,' said the sergeant.

'Would you have any objection?'

'It's not up to me.'

'Right you are, then.' Eric slapped me on the back, not boisterously but as though he was bracing me for bad news. 'I'd like you to start here next week. D'you think you could manage that?'

'I expect so.'

'He won't like it,' said the sergeant once again.

'He doesn't have to like it,' I said. 'I'll just have to try and stay out of his way.'

The sergeant sighed. 'Watch out for your shins. He's got a nasty temper, has Nobby.'

I remembered his warning the following Monday when I slid into the press box. There was no sign of Nobby Clark, but half way through the morning as I was taking note of a case of assault in which a West Indian landlord had bitten off the ear of his tenant, I registered the foxy smell of old clothes and dirt and, without a word, Nobby barged past me to take his corner seat. I held my breath and tried not to yelp as he hacked my ankles in passing. He did not settle immediately, but made a ceremony out of arranging the skirt of his jacket so that it was not rucked up behind him and aligning his pen and copy pad in the exact centre of the desk so that they invaded the space which should have been mine. Between each manoeuvre he looked at me balefully, as if daring me to object.

I said nothing and tried to concentrate on the magistrate's summing-up. The West Indian was remanded in custody for a week and I backed out of the court to phone the story through to the office. When I returned I found that Nobby had spread a pile of papers along the seat. 'Do you mind?' I whispered. 'I can't get in.'

He shot me a glance of pure hatred and moved the papers a fraction of an inch. 'There's not enough room,' I whispered more loudly than before.

He pretended not to have heard, but when I sat down he grabbed the papers from beneath my thigh and stood up to rearrange them. The performance took several minutes and the magistrate's clerk swung round in his chair to see where the noise was coming from. He waited while Nobby stowed one sheaf of papers into an envelope and spread the contents of another envelope along the desk. 'Mr Clark,' he said. 'You are interrupting the business of the court.'

Nobby bowed his head and sat down again. 'Your fault,' he muttered and I saw the boot nearest to me flick sideways towards my ankle. I raised my foot and his own ankle rapped against the edge of my shoe.

'Sorry,' I said.

For a moment I thought he was going to hit me. His pale face turned even paler beneath the stubble and the dirt and his body smell intensified as if, like a civet, he had signalled his rage by squirting musk into his clothes.

Half an hour later the business of the morning came to an end and we stood up while the magistrate left the court. 'Let's get this straight,' I said. 'I know you don't want me here and I don't blame you. But I'm staying and there's nothing you can do about it. We can get on or we can stay out of each other's way. You can please yourself.'

I had not intended to make a speech but the alternative seemed to be to enter into a kicking competition with an old and infirm man. I inclined away from his feet and watched him tremble. It was ludicrous and pathetic. I wished that I had not agreed to do the job. I longed for him to make some conciliatory gesture. But Nobby simply stood and vibrated, his eyes fixed on the wall ahead. It was like being made privy to some shameful illness which came and went without bidding or cure. I felt I was an intruder. 'Can I get you something?' I asked. 'A glass of water. Anything.'

He shook his head slowly.

'I can go to the pub if you want something stronger.'

'Go away.'

'I'll be back,' I said. 'I work here now.'

He gave no sign of having heard me but as I turned towards the door he sighed as if he was surrendering the last breath of air in his lungs. 'I've been here thirty years,' he said. He was not telling me but reminding himself. He sounded puzzled rather than proprietorial. 'Thirty years,' he said. 'It's a long time.'

We did not become friends, but over the next few weeks he came to accept me. He no longer kicked my ankles as he shuffled into the press box. He allowed me space for my notebook. Once he even supplied me with the name and address of a defendant whose charge sheet I had not seen. For my part, I learned to tolerate his smell which became progressively more rancid throughout the month until, for reasons known only to himself, Nobby would bath and change and for a while conform to normal standards of hygiene. Relief did not last for long. The cycle was resumed and after three or four days Nobby was as rank and insanitary as ever.

As Eric had anticipated the court turned out to be a profitable enterprise. The fact did not go unnoticed and one day I arrived to find another reporter in the press box. His name, he said, was Terry Croft and he was from the East London News Agency. I felt the same outrage that Nobby must have experienced when Eric made his appearance. 'Don't blame me,' he said. 'The *News* asked us to cover for them.'

'But we're on a retainer.'

'Can't help that. I go where I'm sent.'

'Have you met Nobby?'

'Not yet. Why?'

'You've got a treat coming.'

Terry's arrival transformed me into Nobby's ally and from a suitable distance I watched him wage the same campaign of hacking and harassment to which I had been subjected when I first came to Thames.

'If he kicks me once more I'll break his bloody neck,' said Terry.

'You can't do that, he's an ancient monument.'

'Then I'll demolish him.'

Terry planned to emigrate to America and he dressed in anticipation of the move in button-down shirts and a US Army surplus jacket. His hair was crew-cut, he chewed gum and smoked Sweet Caporal which he purchased at an exorbitant price from a black-market tobacconist in Hackney. He was good company, but he never allowed me to forget that we were competitors.

There was a chronic lack of phone-boxes in the area and getting a story to the office for them to transmit to the three evening papers was a problem we shared. 'There's no point in cutting each other's throats,' said Terry. 'Let's try and work something out.' His immediate solution was to dismantle the phone on the bomb site opposite the court by removing a magnetic plate from within the mouthpiece. It was easily replaced. But with the plate missing it was out of order for other would-be users. We took turns in reserving it for our private convenience, but giving away the advantage was more than either of us could bear.

In a café across the road I met the manager of a rag shop whose premises in a derelict house nearby were packed from floor to ceiling with old clothes. They were graded roughly into piles of wool and cotton. Eventually they would be shredded and reprocessed, but it was hard to imagine any new fabric emerging from the mountains that rose from the bare boards and lino. They reminded me of photographs taken in the ante-rooms of the gas chambers at Auschwitz. The clothes, I felt, had not been abandoned. Their owners believed they were coming back to claim them. But now they belonged to dead men. It was not a house I entered gladly. But in a corner of what had once been the living room there was a telephone which I rented for £1 a week. I enjoyed its exclusive use until Terry offered £2. 'It's private enterprise,' he said when I protested. 'Competition's good for business.'

'What was all that about not cutting each other's throats?'

'That was then,' said Terry. 'This is now.'

Eventually we established a network of telephones for our mutual convenience: one in the pub, one in the warrant office of the court (only to be used in the direst emergency), one in a kosher butcher's in Commercial Road. My expenses doubled and trebled. 'But it's worth it,' I told Eric. 'You're getting your copy in good time.'

Without any prompting by me he raised my salary by £1 a week. I was still unable to save anything, but now I could at least afford to buy the occasional drink when I accompanied the Mulligan band on their gigs around London. Because I lived with Bob I travelled with him in Mulligan's car. It meant free transport, but it was an uneasy arrangement. Strictly speaking, only girls and musicians were entitled to seats in the car and I constantly felt obliged to do something which would justify my taking up the space. Heading for Perivale one evening Mick wondered aloud whether the band should take on a singer and I rose to the bait.

'How about me,' I said.

Bob looked appalled and Mulligan glanced over his shoulder. 'Didn't know you could sing, cock.'

'I've done a bit,' I said. For slightly less than six months I had been a solo treble in the school choir and subsequently I had sung in one or two camp shows. I was careful not to specify my engagements: they were not likely to impress anyone. But, as Mulligan himself had remarked, the band was not yet professional and their reputation would come to no harm by giving a chance to one more enthusiastic amateur.

'You can try a couple of songs tonight,' said Mick. 'What do you know?'

My repertoire, such as it was, leaned heavily on Sinatra records learned by heart and Bing Crosby standards. But I knew better than to admit it. Something earthier was called for, the only proviso being that the band knew it too. 'How about *Careless Love*?' I said.

Mike drummed on the steering wheel and finally nodded. 'We can stagger through that. What else?'

'*Riverboat Shuffle*?'

He sucked in his breath. 'Too tricky.'

'*Butter and Egg Man*?'

'Not a chance.'

'*Bill Bailey*?'

'You're on,' said Mick. 'What key d'you fancy? As if it mattered.'

My nerve held out until the band was half way through their first set. It was another youth club engagement and they were playing in a hall whose amenities did not include a bar. We had stopped on the way for several pints but I felt in need of several more. The piano was out of tune and as Bob blew a clinker during his solo on *The Saints Go Marching In* he glared at the rickety upright as if it was to blame. There were a dozen or so couples on the floor and I saw Mulligan concentrating on one girl whose skirt lifted in a perfect hoop when she spun round at her partner's finger-tips, exhibiting a vee of pale blue pants. Locating what he called 'a flash' was Mulligan's obsession and it seriously interfered with his playing. He never went so far as to forget the tune, but often his attention wandered and he had been known to drift into another chorus when the rest of the band was preparing to make an end of it after the traditional twelve bars.

The Saints were laid to rest and Mick beckoned me
on to the band-stand. 'All right, cock?' he said.
'All right.'
We were on a higher level than I had imagined. The
upturned faces on the dance floor were like mirrors re-
flecting not images, but light, and without meaning to,
I began to count them until I heard Mick stamp his foot
three times and the band led into the sweet, sauntering
blues whose words, I suddenly realised, had gone from
my mind. They returned just as unexpectedly and leaning
back with my eyes closed – an affectation which excused
me from looking at my audience – I sang about lost love
in another time and place. Opening my eyes for the final
chorus I saw that a small circle of girls had gathered
at my feet. They swayed in time to the music, dancing
on the spot and jiggling gently beneath their loose sweaters. Were they fans? I wondered. Would they want to
touch me? Would I be able to take my pick of the bunch
as Mulligan did? The song ended. They clapped per-
functorily and later on when I sang *Bill Bailey*, Mick tore
straight into the next number without allowing time for
any applause.
My feelings were ruffled if not exactly hurt, but I said
nothing until we were driving home when I asked Mick
how he thought I had done. 'Not bad, cock,' he said.
'But it's not really your sort of thing.'
'Why not?'
'Well, it's not the Hammersmith Palais, is it?'
'I don't know what you mean.'
Mick spotted the blue light of a police car ahead and
reduced his speed. 'Style,' he said. 'The voice is all right.
But it's not authentic.'
I understood what he meant when George Melly turned
up for a band rehearsal the following week. In the suburban litter of Mulligan's sitting room he recreated the New
Orleans of forty years before. Strutting on the Axminster,
cigarette fuming between his fingers, he became the
pimp, the gambler, the sporting-house man. His repertoire was inexhaustible, his performance uninhibited. It

was not authentic in the sense that George had actually
soaked up the tradition in Storeyville or met the girls
at Lulu White's. But it was unmistakably right in spirit.
His exhibitionism was an act of homage. I studied his
gentian-smudged face and the tight arse of his trousers
and wondered how a son of Liverpool, educated at Stowe
could sound so black.

'It's simply how you feel,' he said, when I asked him.

'Really?' I said. I learned later that George listened to
Bessie Smith records as intently as I listened to Sinatra,
mimicking each breath, each angry growl. But he repro-
duced more than the sound. Each song became a dramatic
recitation, a mime, a piece of theatre which he refined
or embellished as he went along. His first version of
Frankie and Johnny ended quite sedately with George reeling round the stage, his hands clasped to imaginary bullet
wounds and expiring at Mulligan's feet. But after he had
worked on it for a while he made his death plunge from
the edge of the stage to the dance floor, toppling like
a felled pine, scattering the dancers as he went. In some
halls the stages were dangerously high and watching
George take his dive I expected him to sustain at least
severe bruises, if not a broken neck. But he never came
to harm. It was as though he was protected by his own
energy which surrounded him like yolk within an elastic
membrane.

His recruitment raised the intellectual tone of the band
by several notches and the band itself provided George
with a captive audience who he would lecture on the
new society which would result when anarchism came
into its own. He had a touching belief in the power
of the word and developed a scenario in which a revolution would start with a single man marching down the
street shouting 'Fuck!'

'Just imagine,' said Geroge. 'One man to begin with.
Then two, then a dozen. Pretty soon there'd be an army.
All of them chanting just one word!' As he went on
to describe it, the walls of the city would shake; Broad-
casting House would disintegrate; the corgis would run

yelping from Buckingham Palace; the government would collapse. 'An end to the constitution,' said George. 'A world of free men.'

'I don't know about that, cock,' said Mulligan, whose political sympathies were unwaveringly conservative. 'You've got to have law and order.'

'Why?'

'Stands to reason.'

'Your reason; not mine.'

'Someone has to make decisions,' said Mulligan. 'You can't have everyone just pissing around. It wouldn't work.'

'Why not?'

Mulligan eased the car to the side of the road. We were driving through Epping Forest on our way back from a gig and it was around two o'clock in the morning. 'I've made the decision to stop,' he said. 'Whatever you lot have to say we're stuck here until I decide to move on.'

He removed the key from the ignition and lit a cigarette. Above and ahead of us the trees waved ghostly branches and a light rain pebbled the windscreen. 'You're proving nothing,' said George.

Mulligan wound down the window half an inch and let the smoke leak away. 'Someone has to make the decision,' he said. 'Am I right?'

We looked out at the rainy night. 'Right,' I said.

'Am I right George?'

'Right,' said George. 'You're also a fascist.'

'Bollocks,' said Mulligan. He restarted the engine and in the glow from the dashboard I saw that he was grinning broadly. Mick was an enthusiastic debater who would, if necessary, pursue an argument for days. But there were times – and this was one of them – when he went for the quick kill. He treated George as an exotic specimen whose views were as entertaining as they were bizarre and Mick relished their unorthodoxy. He was baffled by George's declared sexual preferences and preferred to believe that it was only a matter of time before he came round to more conventional couplings. He was quite uncensorious, however, and his curiosity was insatiable. What he wanted to know was who did what to whom and how did it feel? And George was quite prepared to tell him.

We were all experimenting with sensation and with frankness. To shock was to score a point and to save face it was policy to appear unimpressed whatever the provocation. George did his best to scandalize, but at the same time he was also deeply serious about his work at the gallery where he now held the title of Assistant Curator. The first show he arranged was an exhibition of work by a young Scottish surrealist painter and we were all urged to pay it a visit. 'In fact,' said George 'you can have your own private show.'

The invitation was too flattering to refuse. But he suggested an evening when we had gone to the London Jazz Club, with frequent intermissions in the Blue Posts, an adjacent pub whose draught bitter tasted mysteriously of onions. By the time we reached the gallery my judgement had been replaced by a dangerous euphoria. All the pictures looked wonderful. I stood swaying in front of a composition made up of cubes and scarlet diagonals and decided that I must have it.

'The trouble is,' I confessed. 'I've got no money.'

'We can come to an arrangement,' said George.

'How do you mean?'

'You can buy it on HP. So much a week. If you're certain you want it.'

I thought of Mulligan's portfolio of Max Ernst etchings and the pictures on the walls of George's room and the urge to join the ranks of collectors was overwhelming. George produced a form of agreement which I signed. I went back to look at the picture and proudly gummed the red dot which signified that it was mine in the bottom right hand corner.

'You can collect it next week when the show closes,' said George. 'Right after the first instalment.'

It was the gentlest of reminders that pleasure brought

with it responsibilities. But at the end of a month the pleasure had entirely disappeared. I knew that I had bought the picture for the wrong reason. I liked it well enough, but not sufficiently to pay my weekly dole without protest. Hanging in my bedroom at Ealing it reminded me each time I saw it that I had been trying to copy part of someone else's life and that, in the first place, imitation was pathetic and, in the second place, beyond my means. I sold the picture back to the gallery for less than half what I paid for it and thereafter I listened more critically when George extolled the work of any artist who came under his wing. His eccentricity, I decided, was as well judged as his performances on stage and what he chose to hide was not the perversity which others might disguise, but a shrewd head for business. I liked him no less for it. In fact it seemed endearing to me that the secret side to his nature was one which Dale Carnegie would have endorsed. George, in turn, bore me no ill-will for having returned the picture to the gallery. He was sympathetic about the high cost of art. 'But the only way you'll get paintings cheap is to buy them from the artist,' he told me.

Weeks later I remembered what he said when I met John Minton at a rendezvous for afternoon drinkers called the Caribbean Club. It was approached up a reeking staircase in a building next to the Windmill Theatre and I had been invited there by a friend of Mulligan's named Bill Maddocks who was unusual among the band's supporters for owning a car and buying considerably more than his fair share of drinks. He had served in the army with Mick and was now cheerfully settling in with a firm of stockbrokers in the City. His good temper was phenomenal and he could always be relied on to ferry home drunken musicians or their abandoned girls. Someone had told him that I wrote poetry and one evening in the Blue Posts when George was proclaiming the gospel of surrealism, Bill confessed to me that it was all beyond him and that the writer he preferred was John Masefield.

'I suppose that's frightfully square,' he said. 'But I can't help it.'

'Which poem d'you like best?'

'Actually,' said Bill. 'I rather like *Sea Fever*. The one about the ships.'

'You mean *Cargoes*.'

'That's right. I like both of them as a matter of fact.' He smiled apologetically. 'Frightful, isn't it?'

'Of course not,' I said. 'It's up to you what you like.'

'I suppose it is.'

I decided not to tell him about the picture I had bought and resold. Bill saw me as a fellow spirit and I did not wish to appear fickle. Apart from Masefield, however, we seemed to have little in common. He was keen on rugby ('Just another rugger bugger' was how he described himself). He had attended a minor public school and still wore his old school tie. His father was dead and he lived with his widowed mother to whom he was deeply attached. Our birthdays were within weeks of each other, but in his courtesy and kindness, he seemed to me somehow middle-aged. His job, he told me, was far from demanding and he was usually free by the late afternoon. 'That's when I toddle out for a little drink,' he said. 'Why don't we meet up one day.'

He chose the Caribbean Club because he thought I might find it amusing. 'There are some frightfully pretty girls there,' he said. 'They make one exceedingly welcome.'

'Are they tarts?' I enquired.

He smiled vaguely. 'I couldn't say. I've never asked them. I suppose they are. You don't mind, do you?'

'I don't mind,' I said.

The Caribbean Club was run by West Indians and at least half its customers were West Indian ponces, two of whom I had seen in the dock at Clerkenwell. They sat at the end of the bar beneath a cradle of coloured lights, their cuff-links flashing, their faces dissolving in the darkness of the room behind them. In one corner there was a small band-stand and around a patch of bare floor there were a dozen or more tables and chairs. At four o'clock in the afternoon there were no girls, but sitting alone at a table by the door was a tall, thin man in a striped jersey whose hair fell over his forehead like a streak of tar.

'That's John Minton,' I said. 'He's a painter.'

'He's a bit pissed,' said Bill.

'He often is.'

Minton was a regular at the London Jazz Club where he danced under the noses of the band, ducking beneath the trumpet and dodging the slide trombone like a matador flirting with the horns of the bull which might one day kill him. Like George, who danced in much the same way, he made his pleasure look dangerous. I envied their abandon. They were possessed by the music, or at least gave the impression that they were. Their faces poured with sweat. Their arms and legs jerked at odd angles like splintered broomsticks. They threw back their heads, their expressions rapt, as though they were being addressed by the godhead. They were shamans, semaphoring their spells. They ignored their partners except for occasionally thrusting against their hands to borrow the impetus for still wilder gyrations. I had never seen Minton alone before. Usually he was the centre of a large and boisterous crowd and in his isolation he looked desolate. He dipped his finger in a puddle of spilled drink on the table top and drew the outline of a face. It was like one of his illustrations; a sailor or a shepherd boy. With the flat of his hand he wiped it out and stared at the blank formica.

'I'll see if he'd like a grog,' said Bill.

It was his instinctive reaction to unhappiness. He did not believe that drink actually solved problems, but he saw it both as an anodyne and a token of his good-will. Minton raised his head and the grooves in his cheeks looked like the long pleats in a skirt. He nodded solemnly and a bottle of red wine was brought to the table. He drank two glasses, one after the other, then joined us at the bar.

'Good of you,' he said.

Bill raised his own glass. 'Not at all.'

'I like your work,' I told Minton.

His fingers pattered along the bar as if they were trying to find a way out. 'I should be working now,' he said. 'I shouldn't be here, but I have been abandoned.'

'Bad luck,' said Bill.

'Rotten sod,' said Minton. 'Totally abandoned.' The grooves in his face deepened still further, intensifying what one writer had described as his El Greco look. 'I should go home,' he said. 'Wherever that is.'

'Can you manage?' asked Bill.

Minton poured himself more wine. 'Perfectly.'

It was not the occasion to enquire about his work, but he had already provided the excuse. 'What are you working on?' I asked.

He did not reply at once, but nodded at the lights above his head. They formed an irregular halo and for a moment he looked transfigured. 'Fucking cook books,' he said. 'I'm drawing pictures for cook books.' He poured the final glass and drained it, then shook our hands in turn.

Bill retrieved a pea-jacket from the back of his chair and draped it round Minton's shoulders. 'You're sure you'll be all right?'

'Quite sure,' said Minton. He swished through the bead curtain that masked the exit and disappeared down the stairs.

'What a frightfully nice chap,' said Bill. 'D'you think I should have driven him home?'

The longer I knew Bill, the more I liked him but I found it difficult to understand why he made the band's activities the hub of his social life. 'It's jolly good fun,' he said when I asked him.

'But you don't like jazz much.'

'I like the chaps.'

'You don't do much screwing around.'

'None, actually,' said Bill. 'I don't care for that sort of thing.'

'You're not queer?'

'Certainly not,' he said. 'I simply like being around where people are having a good time. And there's Mick. You can't help being fond of Mick.'

He was right, of course. Mick provided excitement and entertainment. He made things happen. I saw him sometimes as Master of the Revels, self-appointed to lead the faithful out of boredom into light. But he also prevented work being done. I had begun to write poetry again, as well as trying to sell articles to a variety of magazines and Mick offered distractions which I could not afford.

'I take the point,' said Bill. 'But it's different for me. There's nothing else I want to be doing. I like to go along.'

It was useless to tell him that quite often he was exploited, because the pleasure he derived from being of service outweighed any fleeting inconvenience. Bill liked to help people. He enjoyed being part of the background. In a way it was a measure of acceptance. He did not think of himself as inconsequential, but he preferred to be inconspicuous. In his own words, he made up the numbers. When Mick suggested that he went with him on a business trip to France to share the expenses and the driving he did not hesitate. 'Smashing,' he said. 'Fleshpots and plonk. Couldn't be better.'

The plan was to drive from Paris, down to Lyons and through the Jura into Switzerland. 'We'll be gone for a week,' said Mick. 'Everybody practice while we're away.'

Four nights later Bob and I were round at Thea's when there was a call from Geneva. It was Mick on the line. There had been an accident in the mountains, he said. Bill had been driving while he and another passenger were asleep in the back. The car had hit a patch of ice and careered off the road. 'I woke up going arse over tip,' said Mick. 'Couldn't think what was happening.'

'Are you hurt?' asked Bob.

'Nothing serious. We were all right in the back. It was probably being asleep that saved us. There's nothing broken.'

'What about Bill?'

There was a pause long enough for Mick to light a cigarette. 'Poor old sod,' he said, blowing smoke into the pure Swiss air. 'Bill's dead.'

Nine

MONTHS LATER when we talked about Bill it was like trying to recall someone we had met at a party. The memory was agreeable, but faint. I found that I could summon up his face and his smile, but it was never in the foreground and what he had said was, for the most part, reduced to a friendly buzz which always signified assent. The sharpest recollections were like photographs in an album in which Bill was frozen in the act of laughing or drinking. The activity was invariably social. One of his favourite tunes had been Muggsy Spanier's recording of *At the Jazz Band Ball* and whenever I heard it I could see Bill leaning forward with his ear cocked to Spanier's stabbing cornet, his right foot tapping out the beat and the beer shuddering in his glass. He would never dance. 'I'm a fool on the floor,' he explained. But it was not a matter for regret. Bill did not feel left out. Being there made him a participant. His death made no difference to the routine we followed. The ball went on. The ranks closed. The background of which he had been an amiable part remained as compact as it had ever been.

Changes, however, were on the way. On New Year's Day 1949 I woke up in bed with a girl named Jenny and asked her to marry me. It was not a sudden decision. I had known Jenny for three months. She was a cousin of Thea's and stayed with her when she came to London from Colchester where she lived with her husband and two children, a boy and a girl. Her marriage, she told me, was on its last legs. She had agreed to go with her husband to Canada to help him establish a business which would import Scottish knitwear. 'But all I'm giving it is six months,' she said. 'After that I'm leaving him.'

'What about the children?'

'They come with me,' she said. 'Anyone who takes me on takes them on too.'

It was a prospect which I viewed with mixed feelings. I had first gone to bed with Jenny because she was an attractive and seemingly unattached woman who asked for no commitments, no deeper involvement. She was several years older than me and when she described her life – nursing during the war, then training as a physiotherapist – I was reassured, not only by its usefulness but by Jenny's determination to let none of her time go to waste. She was competent in all that she did. Making love with her was brisk, friendly and comprehensive. She gave pleasure and expected it in return. She liked to organise and plan ahead, but her programmes were not rigid. She was bold and she was adaptable. I felt there was no problem she could not solve, no emergency she could not handle.

'I'm not your responsibility,' she told me. 'You don't have to worry. I can look after myself.'

'I want to look after you.'

She smiled indulgently. 'I'll bear it in mind.'

I meant what I said, but my impulse was earthed in the belief that Jenny would not expect me to follow through. 'I've been through the wars,' she said once. And leaning over her in the double bed she made her own when she stayed with Thea, I felt I was allied to a survivor whose experience would now serve us both.

She had thick, lion-coloured hair, cut short and bristling like fur. Her breasts had been mauled by children and her inner thighs were silvered by stretch marks. 'Don't look,' she said. But I admired each scar and blemish as if they were medals awarded for courage in the field. Her husband's name was Alec and I was shocked by the intensity of her dislike for him. They had met, she told me, soon after her fiancé had been killed when his plane was shot down in the North Sea. 'I didn't care what happened to me,' she said. 'I didn't want to marry him, but he got me pregnant. So there we were.'

'Accidents happen.'

'It was no accident,' said Jenny. 'He'd worked it all out. It was the only way he could get me.'

'You could have had an abortion.'

She shook her head. 'Not another. I'd already been through that. It wasn't their fault.'

I thought of Alice, and Emma's resolve to keep her safe. 'You love them now,' I said.

'I've always loved them,' said Jenny. 'I'll never let them go. Whatever happens we'll stay together.'

Our affair began casually. The Magnolias were playing at a club in Cranley, the stronghold of a group of traditionalists who believed that only music made before electrical recordings was the genuine article, and all Mulligan's supporters had been rallied to counter the opposition. Jenny was staying with Thea and we drove to the gig in Mick's car packed into the back with an assortment of instruments including half the drum kit.

'For Christ's sake be careful,' said Mick. 'Let's get it there in one piece.'

Bob sat in the passenger seat and Jenny and Thea shared my lap. I breathed in their mingled perfumes and felt them slither across my thighs when Mick changed gear, as if they were attached to silk runners. Thea squealed and grabbed me around the neck. 'Mustn't do you an injury,' she said.

'It's all right.'

'Are we cutting off the circulation?'

'Not yet.'

'Jenny could give you a massage. She's trained for it.'

'I'll remember that,' I said. 'It might come in handy.'

Jenny was twice the weight of Thea and I tried to ease myself back so that I could support her with my right arm. 'I'm sorry,' she said, 'you must be squashed to death.'

'I can manage.'

'He's not complaining,' said Thea. 'He's got the two of us where he wants us.' She giggled happily and Bob swung round to see what was going on. 'You mind your own business,' she said. 'We're enjoying ourselves.'

I groaned inwardly. By the time we reached the club the chances were that Bob's suspicions would be on the boil and the rest of the evening would be spent avoiding contact with Thea who would then complain that no one was paying her any attention.

As it turned out her aggravation was overshadowed by rival factions at the club, each of them loudly proclaiming their musical preferences. Not only were there the Cranley purists who scorned the Magnolias' use of a double bass instead of a tuba, there were also mainstreamers who would go so far as to allow a saxophone in the line-up. And there was the Mulligan/Melly contingent, broadly revivalist, who endorsed George's gospel that good-time music should be allowed to absorb whatever elements it chose.

The differences were real and keenly felt. The hero of the fundamentalists was a bearded trumpet player named Ken Colyer who had actually worked his passage to New Orleans as a merchant seaman and played with many of the old jazzmen. His trumpet tone was thin and quavery, but for all its imperfections it was the true voice of a tradition and Colyer was its prophet. The mainstreamers were prepared to admit white musicians such as Eddie Condon, Bix Beiderbecke and Jack Teagarden on to the pantheon, while Mick was heart and soul a Louis Armstrong man and George – who was soon to record a popular song of the twenties called *My Canary Has Circles Under His Eyes* – went even further in blurring the musical distinctions.

For them the sound mattered more than the label attached to it. And even more important was the spirit it engendered. 'For Christ's sake,' said Mick, protesting to no one in particular, 'it's supposed to make you feel good.' It was not a point of view which was shared by the sterner partisans, although Cranley was not a typical Magnolia audience. Mick's followers were not purists. They were ravers who enjoyed the band's music and saw the band itself – raffish, randy and anarchic – as the spearhead in a revolt against years of austerity.

The club met in a large hall next to a pub. The bandstand and the bar were at opposite ends and there was a double line of small tables along the facing walls. The Cranley regulars took up their position on one side. The Mulligan supporters stationed themselves opposite and the mainstreamers circulated at either end. Jenny slipped me a pound note and asked me to buy a round of drinks.

'There's no need for that,' I said.

'Yes there is. I know how much you get paid.'

'Gin and orange for me,' said Thea. 'Ask if they've got any ice.'

Jenny drank beer. It was a point in her favour, I decided. In the course of a long evening, Thea's taste for spirits made an appreciable dent in anyone's budget. 'If you want to dance with me,' said Jenny, 'it'll have to be in a corner. I'm not going out there with that lot.'

She gestured towards the floor, now wholly occupied by ravers. Their dancing styles varied but, whatever the variations, all of them performed a curious hopping step which reminded me of a film I had seen of Masai warriors at a tribal enthronement. This was another tribe, I thought. Few of the dancers were over twenty. Most of the girls had sooty eyes and wore black sweaters. Their partners wore thicker, roll-neck sweaters or white shirts open to the waist. Their bare chests streamed with sweat and their shirt sleeves flailed the air.

When I danced I stuck to a modified jive which I had learned from Frank Burdge who I frequently met at the London Jazz Club and who sometimes joined us on Magnolia occasions. It was an act of pure friendship on his part. Frank's musical tastes were more sophisticated than mine. He talked knowledgeably of bebop and chord progression and flattened fifths and admired performers such as Dizzy Gillespie and Charlie Parker. His spiritual home was not New Orleans but 52nd Street, New York and both his idiom and his style of dress was, in the emerging phrase, cool. He was the first man I knew to wear the devastating combination of charcoal grey suit, pink Oxford button-down shirt and black knitted tie. His fiancée – a trim and quietly ribald girl named Kaye – was equally composed in her scarlet sweater and grey pencil skirt. Her hair was swept up into a cornet and her lips looked as though they had been embossed on her pale face. When he was introduced to her, Mick made the mandatory lunge, but it was half-hearted as if he knew that such a trim and well co-ordinated creature had different desires and ambitions.

Frank and Kaye were perfectly matched. They danced together like component parts of a machine which obeyed the beat but ignored its excitement. Nothing seemed to impress them. They rarely looked at each other or even smiled, but their movements were as exact and assured as if they could spell out the most complicated steps telepathically or in a code which no outsider could intercept. Their chosen patch of dance floor was perhaps four foot square. Frank controlled operations from one corner where he stood switching his hips, his right hand extended as limply as a dog's paw, while Kaye gyrated from it, spinning backwards and forwards as if, line by line, she was filling in the clues to a crossword. When the number came to an end they sat down abruptly and took up the conversation where it had been left off. Neither of them was ever in the least out of breath.

'I can't do that either,' said Jenny when I tried to steer her through the Burdge routine. 'You'd better find someone else.'

'I'm not that bothered.'

'It's like doing maths,' said Jenny. 'I can't think when I dance.'

'Nor can I.'

We sat and listened to the music. When George came on to sing the Cranley crowd began a slow hand-clap. The Mulligan supporters sauntered across the floor and tried to look menacing and I wondered if I was going to be called on to demonstrate my loyalty. I hoped not. Punch-ups were rare. Jazz enthusiasts were, by nature, both liberal and lenient and I had only occasionally seen blood flow. But the Cranley barracking went on and on and although George seemed unworried I could see that Mick's patience was wearing thin. The leader of the Cranley pack advanced to the stage and clapped his hands under the bell of Mick's trumpet. Mick goggled over the brass rim and his face turned an even richer shade of puce. When he was straining for high notes the veins on his forehead bulged alarmingly, but it was rage that engorged them now. I half rose from my seat, but Jenny pulled me back as George stepped in front of the microphone and stooping forward like a child presenting a bouquet, planted a kiss on the Cranley leader's forehead.

The barracking dissolved in applause and George pranced back behind the microphone to sing the final chorus. He bowed extravagantly and blew more kisses to the audience. Under Mick's tutelage I knew that his sex life was taking an increasingly heterosexual turn, but when the occasion demanded it he could, as he cheerfully acknowledged, be as camp as a row of tents.

'When are you going home?' I asked Jenny.

'Tomorrow.'

'You've only just got here.'

'I have to get back to the children.'

'And Alec?'

'He can look after himself,' she said. 'I don't even want to think of him. He brings me out in a rash.' She rolled back the sleeve of her blouse and showed me a faint red freckling on the underside of her arm. 'It's on my chest as well,' she said. 'Like prickly heat.'

'I've got a lotion for that.'

She gave me a long, steady look. 'Have you now?'

We drove back to Thea's with Mulligan and sat listening to records until Gaye came home from the theatre. She collapsed into an armchair and Thea took off her shoes and massaged her feet as if she was coaxing them back to life. Appearing twice nightly, Gaye had little to do on stage except stand still and be admired. But each performance, she said, drained her emotionally and we were required to show respect while her convalescence took its course.

Mulligan was not sympathetic. 'It's like Armistice Day,' he said. 'How about a two minute silence?'

'Fat chance,' said Gaye.

Mulligan brandished his wrist watch and raised a finger. 'Everybody ready? Starting now.'

The two minutes seemed interminable but we waited them out. It was Mick's way of demonstrating that Gaye was protesting too much. When she attempted to get out of the chair he pushed her back and pointed mutely to the minute hand and the distance it had to travel. When the time had elapsed he helped her to her feet. 'Feeling better now?' he enquired.

There was no real sense to the argument, but Mick enjoyed making a point. Sometimes he would persist until Gaye burst into tears. She would run into her bedroom, followed eventually by Mick and for half an hour or so we would hear their voices until the complaints became briefer, the silences extended and the door would close with a positive click. It was the signal for everyone to go to bed.

Jenny and I were left sitting by the fire. 'Well,' I said uncertainly. 'I'd better be off.'

'Is that what you want?'

'No,' I said. 'Of course not.'

'Tell me what you want.'

'To go to bed with you.'

'And what else?'

'What do you think?'

'Say it,' she said. 'So we're in no doubt.'

'To make love to you,' I said.

She smiled and took my hand. 'That's what I wanted to hear.'

The garden of Thea's flat ran down to a railway line where the Underground surfaced and I was awake when the first trains rattled by on their way to London. I felt delicately bruised all over and groaned when I propped myself up on one elbow. 'Stay where you are,' said Jenny.

She rolled me on to my stomach and massaged my neck and shoulders until I could hear the blood singing on its way from my spine to my finger tips. 'How's that?' she asked.

'Wonderful.'

'It's a gift,' she said. 'From me to you.'

She came to London again the following week and we went to the theatre to see *Dark of the Moon*. It was a play about magic in the Ozarks and its hero was a Witch Boy who wreaked sexual havoc in the piney woods until he was butchered by vengeful suitors.

'See what can happen if you're not careful,' said Jenny.

'Not to us.'

'Not if I can help it,' she said.

There was an avenue of lime trees on the way from the station to Thea's flat and when we stopped to kiss on our way home the syrup from the leaves gummed our shoes to the pavement. 'We're stuck here for ever,' I said.

'No such luck.'

'You don't have to go,' I said. 'If you go to Canada you'll never come back. I'll never see you again.'

'I promised Alec. I can't let him down.'

'You don't love him.'

Jenny shook me gently by the shoulders. 'That's not the point. Try to understand. It's not what I want. It's what I have to do. It's part of the bargain.'

'It makes no sense.'

She covered my mouth with her hand. 'It makes perfect sense. You just don't want to hear it. And I've already told you. It's only for six months.'

I was not persuaded. I could not envisage Jenny ever returning to England if she went away. All I could see was the imminent end of an affair which gave me total delight. It was unlike anything I had known before and the thought that the pleasure would soon be curtailed made it sweeter and less and less easy to abandon. I had no moral scruples. I did not know Alec and cared nothing for him. Songs about destiny suddenly made perfect sense; what would be, would be. 'Marry me,' I said on New Year's Day and Jenny said that she would.

'At least,' she said, 'I will when I come back.'

'But I don't want you to go.'

She leaned over me, her skin rosy in the light that filtered through the scarf she had spread over the bedside lamp. 'I've already told you. I have to.'

'I don't know if I can wait that long.'

'Then that'll be that.'

'Don't you want to marry me?'

'You know I do. But I won't break a promise. If it's worth having, it's worth waiting for.' She chucked me under the chin. 'There's a lot to consider. There's the divorce for a start.'

It had barely entered my calculations. Alec was an invisible man whose claims were an inconvenience, but whose legal rights I had never seriously considered. 'He can't make you stay,' I said.

'He can make things difficult.'

'What could he do?'

'He could try to hang on to the children,' said Jenny. 'He could sue you for damages.'

'He wouldn't get much. Not from my salary.'

'That wouldn't stop him trying.' She lay back and put her arms round me. 'Don't be upset. I won't let him make trouble. I know Alec. He has to be approached in the right way. I know what to say.'

She was given no opportunity to say it. Three days after she arrived in Toronto she was presented with a private detective's report which described in detail all our meetings over the preceding six weeks. She wrote to me in a rage and misery: 'He says he'll fight me for the children. He says he'll drag you through the courts. But I won't be beaten. Write to me and tell me you love me.'

I wrote every day for two months, but none of the letters reached Jenny. Alec had intercepted them, although – on Jenny's instructions – they were sent to several addresses. She blamed me for neglecting her. She accused me of not caring. I felt that I was shouting into a void. We both stopped writing. I learned from Thea that there had been an attempt at reconciliation but it had not worked. Only eight months after writing her last angry letter to me, Jenny left Alec to live with a young English emigrant who had arrived in Canada shortly before them. 'You can't blame her,' said Thea. 'It was bound to happen.'

'Will she marry him?'

'I doubt it. But he's the way out.'

'I thought I was.'

'Did you really?' said Thea, cocking her head like some gaudy little bird. 'It's only what you wanted to think. You can't believe it now.'

'Yes, I do,' I said. But even as I spoke I knew she was right. I loved Jenny; that much was true. But privately I acknowledged a sense of reprieve. I had been excused and I was glad of it.

So was my mother who I had warned that it seemed likely I would be named in a divorce petition. 'I don't know what's got into you,' she complained when I broke the news. 'First there was that girl. Now there's this. What will people say?'

'I don't care what they say.'

My mother sniffed loudly. 'Don't care was made to care.'

She had a fund of maxims, remembered from her teaching days, which she could produce on demand. Her response was automatic, but there was no doubting her sincerity. She had at last accepted the fact that I was living and working in London and that there was no likelihood of my returning home. But she never missed the opportunity of reminding me that my moral lapses were the consequence of my desertion. I had rejected the good example of family and friends and eventually I would get my comeuppance.

'Lord knows what your father would have thought,'she said.

'The same as you I expect.'

'And it doesn't bother you?'

'It's my life,' I said. 'I have to make my own mistakes.'

'I only want to be proud of you,' said my mother. 'Don't you see that?'

I was given no credit for the ending of the affair with Jenny. But my mother's relief was undisguised. 'I couldn't have borne it,' she said. 'There's never been a divorce in our family. What we've got is stickability. That's what keeps us together.'

Her loyalty to the clan had increased as her health worsened. Despite severe headaches and failing eyesight she wrote long newsy letters to every brother and sister, near or far. 'It's my job,' she insisted, when I told her to put her pen aside for the night. 'I'm the family scribe.' She sat at the mahogany dining table which glowed redly beneath a century of wax, notes to one side, blotter to the other. Her pen was clasped by a gold band, stamped with her name and the date of her first teaching appointment. 'Dear Joe', she wrote, 'Dear Frank', 'Dear Ada'. They replied with less regularity, but my mother did not blame them for their tardiness. 'They've got other things to do,' she said. 'It's my job to keep everyone in touch.'

My Uncle Frank, with whom I had spent my last summer holiday before the war, was the most faithful of her correspondents. He had moved from Westcliff and now lived with his wife Edna in a bungalow at Rayleigh where he was a director of the local football club. He was my mother's favourite brother, the closest to her in age, and I had pleased her by paying him a visit soon after I moved to Ealing.

Our first meeting had been uneasy. He told me he felt I had let my mother down by refusing to live at home when I left the army. But when I argued, as calmly as I could, that my work was in London and that – like him – my roots were no longer in the Potteries, he changed his mind. Aunt Edna, who was twenty years his junior and had always taken my part, invited me to stay and I spent several weekends sitting with them both in the directors' box at Rayleigh Football Club, and admiring the vast air-raid shelter that occupied one corner of their garden. It was equipped with comfortable bunks and a larder crammed with tinned food and drink.

'We could have sat the war out down here,' said my uncle, showing me a case of Black and White whisky. 'Can't let it go to waste now.' He poured me a glass and we toasted our reconciliation. 'Don't tell your mother,' he said. 'She wouldn't approve.'

Unexpectedly, he died in the late spring of that year and, as my mother's representative, I attended the funeral. It was, I realised, a solemn occasion and as I sat in the train taking me to Essex, I began to worry about the inappropriateness of my clothes. There was no problem with the suit. After my demob trousers had split at the knees I had invested in a made-to-measure, double-breasted outfit in charcoal grey with a thin red line striping the material. The lapels had a gangster sharpness, but the overall impression – or so the tailor assured me – was restrained. I had a white poplin shirt and a black tie. From my head to my ankles I was decently dressed. But the effect was ruined by my shoes – the only pair I owned – which were ornamental brogues, punched and fretted around the toes and coloured an assertive shade of ox-blood.

They would not do I told myself as I stepped off the train, an impression which was confirmed that evening as Aunt Edna and I sat by the fire discussing the arrangements for the funeral next day. 'Did you bring any other shoes with you?' she asked.

'I forgot,' I lied. 'I'm sorry.'

'Not that it matters,' said Aunt Edna. 'But they're a bit bright.'

I studied each toe-cap, pierced like a muffin. 'I could black them over.'

'I don't think it would work,' she said.

'I suppose not.'

We sat there staring at the shoes and to my surprise

my aunt began to giggle. I thought at first that she was crying, then that she was hysterical and I supposed that she had been overcome by grief. I took her hand and squeezed it sympathetically. 'It'll be all right,' I said. 'You'll see.'

She shook her head and laughed out loud. Tears sparkled in her eyes and as she dried them she pointed to my feet. 'Brown boots,' she said.

I knew then what she meant. Among the records stacked beneath the radiogram was a monologue by Stanley Holloway which had been a favourite of my uncle's. It was about a humble mourner at a very grand funeral who was criticised for showing disrespect at the graveside by wearing brown boots. Like me, they were the only ones he had. 'Braahn boots,' said Aunt Edna in Stanley Holloway's voice. And again she laughed until she cried.

'I'll tell you what,' she said at last. 'You could wear some shoes of your Uncle Frank's.'

'Would you mind?'

'Of course I wouldn't. Not if you don't.'

'Not a bit,' I said, although I did have a momentary qualm about dead men's shoes. It vanished the moment I put them on. My uncle and I took the same size and when I walked up and down testing them for comfort, I was reassured by the snugness of the fit.

The only person who disapproved was my Uncle Percy who was also staying the night. Eight years earlier he had been my escort when he delivered me to the Methodist Homes in Lancashire and the memory of that day still troubled us both. I disliked him as much as he disliked me, although I did my best to conceal it. He felt himself under no such constraint and although I was attending the funeral on my mother's behalf, I heard him enquiring loudly when I was out of the room why I had come. 'You can't tell me Frank would have wanted him here,' he said. 'He hardly knew the boy.'

'I want him here,' I heard my Aunt Edna reply. 'And that's quite good enough.'

No one spoke to my Uncle Percy like that. He was no longer a headmaster, but even in his retirement he commanded respect. He could not argue with the widow, especially when the body of her husband was still in the house. But he made his displeasure known by sulking throughout dinner, answering questions in mono-syllables and staring at me crossly over the water jug.

'You could, at least, have brought your own shoes,' he said when my Aunt Edna went out to the kitchen.

'I didn't have any.'

'Don't be ridiculous. You couldn't be bothered.'

Discussion seemed pointless. 'Think what you like,' I said.

'That's always been your attitude. I know what your mother's had to put up with all these years. I'd never have put up with it.'

He wagged the stump of his little finger in my face and panted like an old dog. His nose still reminded me of a cleaver, poised for attack. But it was no longer menac-ing. He could do no injury; he could only grumble. He grumbled for at least an hour when we retired for the night. The lack of space – my aunt in one room, my uncle's body in another – meant that we had to share a double bed. I had a slight but persistent cough which kept us both awake and when, at last, he fell asleep I lay beside him trying to avoid touching his bony toes and measuring the rhythm of his snores.

The funeral service next day was brief and entirely formal. During the war my Uncle Frank had come out of retirement to run a civil service department and his dispatch was as bloodless and efficient as an inter-office transfer. There was an address by a young minister who had never met my uncle and then his coffin slid through a marble slab into the ovens behind the chapel.

'Best way to go,' said my Uncle Percy as he kissed the widow goodbye. 'There's a lot of money goes into a grave. It's not worth the expense.'

His farewell could have been gentler, I thought. But, at least, it was not maudlin. My family did not go in for unnecessary sentiment. Although they complained bitterly about any minor inconvenience, calamity stiffened their sinews. In the faces of disaster they made no fuss.

There was sherry and sandwiches for the mourners, but they had all left by tea-time. I watched their cars roll cautiously down the steep gravel drive and edge out into the main road. 'You'll stay another night, won't you?' said my aunt.

'If you like. I don't want to be any trouble.'

'It's no trouble. I'd rather not be on my own.'

We sat companionably and watched a play on television. 'Your uncle only had it for the sport,' said my aunt. 'It was cricket he liked best.'

'I remember.'

'Do you remember staying with us before the war?' she asked. 'You had a taste of my drink.'

'Gin and It,' I said. 'You told me not to tell my mother.'

'And did you?'

'Of course not.'

The play came to an end and a spinning potter's wheel marked the interval between programmes. 'I don't think you should call me "aunt" any more,' said Aunt Edna. 'It makes me feel ancient.'

'You don't look ancient,' I said. 'I think you look very attractive.' It was true. Her hair was arranged in a glossy brown bob and her long legs gleamed in the firelight. I calculated that she was in her late thirties.

'I've never had a job,' she said. 'What am I going to do now?'

'You don't have to decide that right away.'

She shook her head impatiently and her hair bounced as though it was on springs. 'I know I don't. But it's stupid not to have any idea.'

'You should start a business,' I said. 'Invest in something.'

'Such as?'

I groped for inspiration. 'Start a magazine. Collect a few poems. You could run a salon.'

'It doesn't sound like me.'

'How can you tell. Think of the talent you'd be bringing on.'

She looked at me shrewdly. 'Including you, I suppose.'

'Why not?'

'I don't think so,' said Edna. 'I can only take on something I understand. And all I understand is how to take care of someone. That's what I did with your Uncle Frank. It's all I've ever done.'

There was a hot-water bottle in my bed and a jar of biscuits on the bed-side table. I listened to Edna running taps and opening and closing doors and as I waited for sleep I wondered if I should have said or done anything different. My idea of the magazine had been frivolous. But Edna reminded me of Jenny in her determination not to waste time or opportunity and I had no doubt that, had she taken it up, she would have made it a success. Less than a year later when she married a wealthy builder – scandalising my family, who declared that the period of mourning had been too brief – I sent a letter wishing her luck.

She replied on paper printed with her new husband's business address and although she sent me her love she did not suggest that we met. 'Life is very full,' she wrote. 'I have learned to do the book-keeping and I have never been busier.' There was a post-script: 'I'm glad you have stopped calling me aunt. Sometimes I think about the poets.'

It was how I had begun to think of myself, but without yet having had a single poem published, the description seemed presumptuous. All the same, writing poetry had become an absorbing interest. I stayed at home most evenings, filling page after page of my notebook and at work I spent my lunch hours revising drafts which never reached a final state. When I read the verses aloud they sounded like poor imitations of poets I admired. There was a block between what I felt and how I expressed it. The words themselves were nerveless and second-hand and when I tried to be direct, the sense and structure of the poem became lost in a maze of borrowed styles.

I discussed my difficulties with Peter Stanford who was living at home with his parents at Worcester Park, near Epsom. We had kept in touch since leaving the army and his comments and advice on what I was trying to write had continued week by week in a stream of letters, crackling with criticism of films he had seen, books he had read and art exhibitions he had attended. Peter had views on everything, but he was undecided how he should direct his own life. He hoped to win a place at University, preferably Oxford. But meanwhile, he was uncertain whether he should concentrate on becoming a writer, or a photographer, of if fine art was the form of expression he should pursue.

'Why not settle for just one thing?' I asked.

Peter looked scornful. 'Why should I? Michaelangelo didn't.'

'Michaelangelo was a genius.'

'Genius is an infinite capacity for taking pains.'

'You read that somewhere,' I said. 'It isn't true. If that's all it means we could all qualify.'

Peter took his time. 'Well,' he said after a judicious pause, 'who's to say that we don't?'

His criticism of my poems was of no help, not because he disliked them but while he sympathised with my intentions he had no idea how they could be realised. His own poetry was still lugubrious with images of halted clocks, melting sun-dials and weeping candles – the furniture of time patented by Salvador Dali. But he was also keeping a journal, he told me. It would eventually run to millions of words and provide a comprehensive record of our lives and times. 'Especially my time,' said Peter. 'I'm leaving it to you in my will. Don't forget, you're writing my biography.'

That summer he married a trim, blond ATS sergeant named Kit and I composed an epithalamium for their wedding in which I advised Peter to throw away his sun-dials and abandon his haunted castles for the real world. 'You'll never understand,' he said. 'For me, they are the real world.'

Kit left the army and with part of her gratuity bought an apricot coloured corduroy suit which Peter helped to select. His interests now included designing clothes and he had also started to write a series of plays which reworked the Theban legends in the style of Jean Anouilh. They were not casual undertakings. The full sequence was planned and executed within a few short months and after seeing *The Lady's Not For Burning*, Peter evolved a plan in which he would offer his entire corpus to the actress Pamela Brown in the hope that her enthusiasm and reputation would carry the project into the West End.

Somehow the scheme never materialised. But it occurred to me that there were other ways in which we could put drama to work. While waiting to hear whether or not he had been awarded a place at University, Peter found a job teaching at a school at Epsom. It was called Arden, a word whose bosky associations reflected the healthy-in-mind-and-body philosophy of the establishment. The headmaster was a follower of A.S. Neill and the school was run on libertarian principles which attracted not only parents who thought themselves progressive, but also a number of children whose behaviour was charitably described as 'anti-social'. There were two arsonists, several accomplished thieves and one possible psychopath who, so far, had only cut up cats. 'They're interesting kids,' said Peter. 'They represent a challenge.'

To meet it, he and Kit moved into a flat above the school. I stayed with them often, sleeping on a camp bed in the sitting room. Life at Ealing had soured since my parting with Jenny and when Peter suggested that I should move in while I found somewhere more permanent, I gratefully accepted.

There were many attractions. I liked the town which, despite its commuter status, still had the shabby glitter of a spa to which a king had once brought his mistress. Half a mile from the school the Downs debouched from a sunken road whose steep sides gave no warning of the prospect that lay ahead. Peter and I formed a habit of walking up the road late at night when the wind roared overhead and the moon shone on the bones of dead trees. We frightened ourselves with the thought of a time-slip. 'One night,' promised Peter, 'when we get to the top it won't be land ahead of us, but the sea.' We picked our way over chalk and fossil stones and imagined the ocean reclaiming its lost acres.

I also liked the people attached to the school. Few of the staff had academic qualifications, but there was no doubting their dedication. There was a former grave-digger named Victor who taught woodwork and whose good nature had clearly been developed as an antidote to his earlier job. One day he was splitting logs beneath the living room window while Kit, who was an accomplished pianist, tried to practise a difficult piece. She flung open the window as the rhythm of the axe drowned the tick of her metronome, only to be met by Victor's smiling face. 'Hello, there,' he called cheerfully. 'I'm chopping, you're Chopin. Everybody's chopping!'

Half the pupils lived locally and we were often invited to dinner or to cocktail parties by their parents. There were several of them I found interesting, especially the mother of three small girls who talked intelligently about poetry and asked me to show her what I had written. Her name was Claire and on our second meeting she told me, almost in passing, that she and her husband believed in an open marriage and that she saw morality as an entirely individual matter. It was not an invitation, but I took it as encouragement.

I suggested to Peter that we should collaborate on a play with parts for everyone we wanted to know better. He agreed enthusiastically and over one weekend we wrote a verse drama called *People in Flight*. The action took place on a plane flying from Athens to London and its passengers included a woman of the world who had abandoned her lover, and a cynical journalist escaping a civil war. They were the best parts in the piece and they were played, on the night, by Claire and myself. It was not conceived as a stage production, but as a reading before an invited audience, whose good-will we could take for granted. The reading went well and afterwards I confessed to Claire what its purpose had been. She opened her blue eyes in mock astonishment. 'Go on!' she said.

'You mean that you knew?'

'Darling,' she said in a drawl which she used to mock any declaration which might otherwise sound serious, 'it was never a frightfully deep secret.'

'But you went along with it?'

'Why ever not?' she said. 'It's quite a compliment. Isn't that what you meant it to be?'

I swallowed hard. 'Of course.'

'And that's how I took it.' Claire put her arm through mine and led me towards the door. 'Now let's go home,' she said.

Ten

THE BADMINTON COURT in Claire's garden was bounded on one side by a line of mulberries and on the other by a nut-walk. At the end nearest the house there was an open-air stage on which we performed a summer pantomime and afterwards we hung coloured lights in the trees and drank fruit punch spiked with gin. Bob Dawbarn had brought a pick-up band including Les Rawlings and the clarinettist Monty Sunshine and we danced to the music until the walls shook and the glass shivered in the windows.

It was a perfect house for parties. An Edwardian gentleman had built it and a modern architect had furnished it. Taste plus lack of funds had produced a lucky compromise, so that light varnished the bare floors, and the stairs were carpeted in white canvas which looked luminous at dusk. There was a conservatory leading off the living room and when the parties had passed their peak there was usually a row of recumbent bodies in wicker chairs or stretched out on the settee. One night I fell asleep there and awoke to find that someone had tied a large pair of round metal floats to my ankles and I rejoined the dancers looking like a convict on his way to the rock-pile.

Holding the centre of the floor was Michael Andrews, an artist Peter had first met in the army. He was tall and thin, with a mop of dark brown curls and a sharply pointed nose which jabbed at the ceiling as he threw himself round the room. Mike's wild dancing was in total contrast to his usual demeanour which was gentle and hesitant. He was the most polite painter I had ever met; even when he was engaged in some drunken and passionate debate he would always apologise for swearing. Sometimes, however, he would apologise in advance and having delivered the warning, proceed to have his money's worth of well judged abuse.

He was a student at the Slade and although his first show was still months ahead he was already being discussed admiringly by fellow students. His best paintings were mostly of his family lulled by sunlight on a Norwich lawn, or parables of disaster such as his picture of a man falling down in a busy street. His observations went beyond anecdote and realism. In the world he portrayed the skull smiled courteously beneath the skin. However fair the weather, black skies were always round the corner. Against all his inclinations he was a prophet and because the thought alarmed him he kept it to himself.

'Never admit to more than you have to,' he advised Frank Burdge. 'Not many people listen, anyway. But when they do, they get it wrong.'

Frank nodded glumly. He had decided, after much deliberation, to apply for a grant which would take him to art college and he had asked Mike the best way to go about it. He had brought some of his smaller paintings for us to see and as he propped them, one at a time, against the back of a chair I hoped that someone would warm to their intentions. I did not think it was likely. Two out of three were street scenes. A canal, choppy with ice, loitered beneath an iron bridge. Two tarts gossiped on a corner. They were truthfully and affectionately done, but I doubted whether they would impress any selector.

There was also an extraordinary picture of a tabby cat hanging by its neck from a pole. It looked like a birthday card which had gone gruesomely wrong. 'It's a Mau-Mau warning,' explained Frank. 'They set it up outside the houses of white farmers they want to scare off. I saw the photograph in the *Express*.'

Mike raised his finger. 'Don't say it's a copy. Call it a reference.'

His advice was sound, but Frank was refused the grant.

He took a job with an insurance company and instantly sold policies to most of his friends. 'I don't know what he's like as a painter,' said Bob, slightly dazed after parting with the first premium. 'But he's a bloody good salesman.'

Insurance was not much discussed at Claire's parties, nor was any other kind of business. Her guests were varied and a typical gathering might include Ida and May, two genteel ladies who ran a dancing school in one of Epsom's more sedate streets; a psychiatrist from one of the several mental hospitals that ringed the town; a publisher; a market gardener; a drama therapist; Sam, who installed swimming pools and embarrassed meetings of the local Labour Party by knowing and singing all the words to The Red Flag; the school cook and one or two town planners and architects. Politically they were all inclined to the Left. For years, Claire had tried unsuccessfully to get herself elected on to the Epsom council. But she was at last acknowledging that it was a vain hope.

She had always been a socialist, but her house was used as the meeting place for a communist group – actors, designers and engineers who had escaped from Hitler's Europe and now pondered wretchedly on what their role should be in the nuclear world. Almost without exception the men were short, dark and nattily dressed with gold on their wrists, and scalps which glistened beneath their thinning hair. They played tennis and sunbathed and brought Claire parcels of garlic sausage from Soho, most of which they ate themselves. Few of the women who accompanied them could match their smartness or their vivacity. They wore slacks and Arran sweaters which smelled of armpits and it was they who left piles of petitions demanding peace and unilateral disarmament which we were all required to sign.

At least one English member of the group had begun to worry that his signature might be seen by the wrong people. He was an architect who had joined the party before the war and was now nerving himself to resign.

His work was mainly in overseas development, and a discreet witch-hunt was being conducted in government circles to expel known Reds from positions of influence. Claire encouraged him to break with his communist past. 'For heaven's sake,' she said. 'You were never all that keen.' His principal anxiety, she reminded him, had always been that one day – as a requirement of party discipline – he might be directed to go and sell copies of the *Daily Worker* outside Waterloo Station. He had been spared that. Now it was time to quit altogether.

There was no talk of politics at the parties. Dancing went on until four or five in the morning. Couples who could find beds retired to them and as dawn broke the more robust guests would trail out into the garden to play croquet. The grass was thick with dew and the first balls to roll through it left tracks like tram lines. We picked mulberries and when one fell on to Claire's chest it shattered into pulp the colour of garnets.

I spent all summer with Claire. On Saturdays when I was not working we would meet in the Spread Eagle at Epsom, whose saloon bar looked out on to the market pitched around the clock tower. The stalls were covered with coloured canopies which threw a soft dazzle on to the brass top of the bar. The reflections swam round the room like fish and I watched them swarm up and down the column of Claire's throat and shoal in the long valley of her back. She wore dresses which were secured by only two or three buttons. On hot days in the garden we went naked. The nuts ripened and pattered down on to my notebook. I was writing love poems in which, at last, I seemed to hear my own voice. 'Darling,' said Claire, when I showed them to her. 'It's no use asking me what I think. If they're about me, of course I shall like them.'

I read them aloud at a poetry group formed by Hubert Nicholson, a sub-editor at Reuters and the author of half a dozen novels and several books of poetry. He was a

Yorkshireman from Hull and his criticism was genial but blunt. 'Lucky bugger,' he said. 'There's no doubt you're having a good time. But you've been reading too much Auden. Look at this and this and this.' He went through each over-ripe lyric, stripping it of adverbs, seizing on false rhymes, questioning assonance and metre and alliteration, shaking it like a terrier with a rat. 'Of course you should celebrate a good fuck,' he said. 'But do it right. Honour the occasion with a proper poem.'

My feelings were not hurt. Hubert was the critic I had needed for a long time. However caustic his remarks, his good-will was unmistakable. He could quote pages of Milton and Wordsworth and Keats. He had met Eliot and George Barker and he was a friend of A.S.J. Tessimond, whose much-anthologised poem *Cats* had long been a favourite of mine. His grandfather had attended penny readings in Hull where, in a hired hall he had listened, enthralled, to dramatic renditions of Dickens. Hubert wanted poetry to have the same spell-binding effect. He also believed that, given the encouragement, most people could write poetry, or at least verse. And the group which met every month in his own home not only heard programmes of work by established poets, but made programmes of their own. We brought food and drink and more often than not the end of the meeting was signalled by the party sound of an Armstrong Hot Five record which Hubert slid on to the gramophone. He had met Armstrong during one of his British tours and his feeling for jazz though not profound, was proprietorial.

He was short and plump, with a Van Dyke beard and a lock of hair which he allowed to fall over his left eyebrow so that he could toss it back to emphasise a point during his frequent lectures. He was a didactic man who, uncharacteristically, was open to argument. Above all, though, he was an enthusiast who wanted to share the pleasures of life and literature (the two were not only compatible, he declared, but symbiotic), and each heated discussion would close with Hubert flinging his arms round his opponent as if he wanted to make a gift both of his opinion and his love.

He lived with Barbara, who worked as a cook at Arden School. She had a broad Slav face and fine yellow hair which hugged her forehead and cheekbones like a cap. Her lovely, impassive looks reminded me of a mask or the picture I had seen of a man who had been ritually strangled and then buried in a peat bog in Sweden. When the body was disinterred after centuries his expression was seen to be one not of pain, but contentment. He had gone gladly and he had no regrets.

Barbara displayed the same serenity. But she welcomed life instead of death and was unalarmed by whatever surprises it had to spring. She had three children and, secretly, she was writing a novel. By the time it was published she had become a Catholic convert and her book, warmly endorsed by Graham Greene, was a minor best-seller. Hubert was glad of her success, but as a devout atheist he was suspicious of a novel which was harnessed to a fashionable faith. In Hubert's mythology God was Old Nobodaddy, the fiction first conjured up by William Blake. He was a vain and petulant father figure who doled out more punishments than rewards and sharing a household with such a tyrant imposed a strain which he found hard to bear.

Hubert kept most of his troubles to himself. 'When you think about it,' he said, 'they're nothing compared to Tessi's.' A.S.J. Tessimond worked as a copy-writer for an advertising agency and when we first met he had just produced an ad for Brasso in which a dancing kettle jigged merrily within what appeared to be a frame of solid prose. Reading it I realised that it was, in fact, a poem which led the eye through jokes and concealed rhymes into an amiable soft-sell. 'You can't print it as verse,' said Tessi. 'It frightens them off.'

He seemed depressed by any reminder of the reputation he had made as a poet a decade earlier. That year he had accepted an advance from a publisher to write a set of rhymes to accompany a new edition of *Bewick's*

Birds. As a wholly metropolitan man he had difficulty in distinguishing a thrush from a magpie. Wild life was, for him, an enigma. But he had spent the advance, the deadline was drawing near and the publisher was growing impatient. At Hubert's desk Tessimond sat surrounded by books on bird recognition. He had done a fair job on the osprey that morning, he said, but what in God's name was there to say about the long-tailed tit? 'The trouble with birds,' he reflected 'is that they're not human.'

Tessi was all too human. Shy and slender, with a thatch of straw-coloured hair, he loped from crisis to catastrophe without breaking step. He was sexually impotent, although he was usually accompanied by attractive and admiring women. But his disadvantage drove him to make romantic gestures of such extravagance that few observers were aware of his enduring distress. Riding one day on the upper deck of a bus he saw a beautiful West Indian woman crossing the road below. He jumped off the bus and followed her for half a mile to a basement in Notting Hill where, when he tried to talk his way into the house, knives were levelled at his throat. He pursued another woman all the way to Rome to present her with a bouquet of roses. When I asked him why he went to such extremes he smiled briefly. 'It's instead of a life,' he said.

For several months I had been sending batches of my poems to magazines and receiving them back with depressing regularity. But in 1950 I had my first acceptance. It was from a new poetry broadsheet called *Quarto*. The editor was James Reeves and as well as praising the poem he accepted, he sent me a long letter criticising those he had turned down. 'Sorry about the typing,' he wrote. 'But my eyesight's none too good.'

He was, I subsequently learned, almost blind. Each of the hundreds of poems he received was read aloud to him by his wife. The likely contenders went through repeated readings. 'What listening to poems does,' he wrote to me, 'is point up the stylistic influences. And there's no doubt in my mind that you are reading the wrong people. If you're going to imitate, you should imitate a poet who will tax your capabilities to the utmost.' He sent me a reading list which corroborated most of what Hubert had already said. All moderns, especially Auden and MacNeice, were proscribed. Recommended poets included Wyatt, Hardy and George Herbert. 'Take special note of Hardy,' wrote James Reeves. 'He's a great poet and a favourite of mine. What looks like clumsiness is strength. I would advise you to copy no one. There's no need. You have your own talent. But Hardy can break you of bad habits. Send me more poems when you're ready.'

I took his advice. I thought of him surrounded by manuscripts which he could barely see and of the time he gave to counselling a beginner instead of writing his own poetry. Why he should think it worthwhile I could not imagine; but I was deeply grateful.

Quarto survived for eighteen months and published several more of my poems. It was one of the best of the little magazines and its death was mourned not only by those who wrote for it. But it was only one of many. Every month produced a new crop of publications and the poems which had been rejected by *Stand* went on their way to *Departure* and from there to *Nimbus* or *Listen*. There was also *The Window* which was co-edited by John Sankey and Jean Andrews from an address in Hampstead where I was invited one evening to a party. It was a small, untidy flat in which John stooped like a crane in a cage whose ceiling was several inches too low. He was pale and thin and peered through thick glasses at a crowd of people grabbing for bottles of wine on the kitchen table.

'About your poem,' he murmured. 'Jean and I had a slight disagreement. She thought a couple of lines were rather strong.'

'Strong!' I said. I could not believe he was serious.

The poem was called *The Mediterranean Man* and centred on a priapic hero who was put to death by villagers unable to face the truths he told. 'You remember how it goes?' asked John.

'Of course I do.'

'It's the fifth verse,' he said. And holding his glass as if it was a microphone he began to recite:

> *He took a hundred women*
> *To the woods that night*
> *And notched the village steeple*
> *With the score.*
> *The weathercock swung south*
> *And roses showered from the morning star.'*

'Well?' I demanded.

'It's the hundred women,' said John. 'That and notching the steeple. Jean thought it was a bit much. But I told her it was entirely redeemed by the roses.' He patted my shoulder reassuringly. 'Don't worry,' he said. 'I convinced her. We're printing it as you wrote it.'

'I should bloody well think you are.' I said.

'We hope you'll send us more. We have great plans.'

'Do you really,' I said, still bristling at the possibility of being censored.

'International issues,' said John. 'Guest editors. And more publishing. There's a great future in offset litho. We could centralize the printing of every little magazine in Britain.' Behind his spectacles his eyes gleamed as though he had been granted a vision of the future. I could see the logic of the plan but there seemed something anomalous in the idea of a little magazine tycoon.

'Of course,' he said. 'It won't be for a while. For the time being we have to concentrate on our writers.' He glanced round the room as if he was judging a chorus line. 'Is there anyone you'd like to meet?'

In one corner there was a large lady in a cloak declaiming to an audience which was already beginning to back away. Her name was Iris Orton and she wrote poems which were both lush and empty. 'Not her,' I said.

John caught the sleeve of a man who had already made his escape and was heading for an almost virgin bottle of wine. 'I think you should meet Harold Pinta,' he said.

I remembered the name, partly because of its unusual spelling, and I complimented him on a poem I had seen in the last issue of *The Window*. 'It's not very good,' he said.

'What's wrong with it?'

'Too fussy.'

I had not thought it in the least fussy. It was short, bleak and menacing and I told him so. He sipped his wine and smiled. 'Really,' he said. 'Is that what you think?'

He was easily the best dressed man in the room. He wore a dark shirt and a dark suit. His black shoes were polished. His hair was divided by a neat parting and he was freshly shaved. 'Harold's an actor,' said John. 'He's with a company in Ireland.'

'Was,' said Harold. 'I'm looking around at present.'

'What parts did you play?' I asked.

'Small parts.'

'Which?'

He lit a cheroot as dark as his suit. 'This and that. Nothing in particular.'

He was perfectly friendly, but he hoarded information about himself as though he was keeping it in reserve for an emergency. His reticence made me talk and drink all the more and in what seemed no time at all I found myself lying on the floor with Harold squatting neatly on his heels beside me, a fresh cheroot clipped between his fingers and the room behind him tilting from side to side.

'I'm drunk,' I said.

'Most likely.'

'And what are you doing?'

'As you can see,' said Harold. 'I'm watching.'

Next day I remembered telling him about the agency and complaining how monotonous the work had become. I was saying the same thing to everyone. I sat next to

Nobby Clark in the press-box and wondered how long it would be before my boredom turned to resignation. It was a sum I did not dare compute. There was no reason for me to see Nobby as an object lesson. Our lives were in no way similar. But as we sat on an oak bench, surrounded by oak panelling I imagined that the terminal box was closing in.

For Nobby it suddenly did. He did not put in an appearance for three days and I thought that he might be ill. The sergeant jailer rang round the hospitals and we learned that Nobby had been admitted to Whitechapel after collapsing in the street and that he had died twenty-four hours later.

'Poor old sod,' said Terry Croft.

'Someone should let his family know,' I said.

Eventually it was left to the police at Southend who broke into Nobby's house and found the names and addresses of his children. 'Pathetic really,' said the sergeant. 'He had a cupboard full of corned beef. Three hundred cans of it. They reckon that's what he lived on.'

I was asked to clear out his desk at the court. When I opened it the smell was so strong that it was as though Nobby himself had sat down beside me. I groped inside and brought out a pile of notebooks, copy pads and unopened letters. Nobby had ignored all his mail, regarding it either as irrelevant or interfering, and – especially if it looked in any way official – he had stowed it away instantly, consigning it to oblivion. There were over twenty Income Tax demands and an equal number of cheques from newspapers, dating back two or three years. They totalled more than £500.

'I told you he was rich,' said the sergeant. 'He must have been worth a packet.'

'Who gets it?' asked Terry.

'The family. You'd better let me have those cheques. They're part of the estate.'

At the back of the desk I found a half bottle of whisky. 'They're not getting this,' I said. We drank it in alternate sips, passing the bottle round and wiping it on our sleeves after each swallow.

'Come to think of it,' said the sergeant. 'It's the first time the old bugger's ever bought me a drink.' He stood to attention and clicked his heels. 'Good health,' he said formally. 'Happy landings.'

It was a wet spring and the back room of the office became unusable. The plaster on the walls erupted into huge blisters and pools of water formed on the floor. We took to measuring the spread of damp across the ceiling, pencilling the date against each new tide mark until Eric complained. It was a personal reproach, he felt, and his feelings were hurt. 'I can't help it raining,' he said. 'I don't make the weather.'

In the front room rain also stopped play in the office game known as Mulligan's Fancy. It was so called in homage to Mick's well known obsession with female underwear and it was invented by Bob one idle afternoon when he realised that, sitting at the desk by the window, he had a direct view through the grating to the pavement above. Customers who called at the post office often stopped to chat after conducting their business. Many of them, Bob noted, were women and what they wore beneath their skirts became the subject of a competitive field study in which points were awarded for sightings and the length of time the wearer remained under observation. Briefs and camiknickers scored top marks, but one day I came downstairs to find Bob keeping vigil in a state of ecstasy.

'Did you just pass a girl in a red dress?' he demanded.

'That's right. Heading for King's Cross.'

'What was she like?'

I had not really noticed. 'Dark,' I said.

'Was she young?'

'I think so. In her twenties.'

'Pretty?'

'Fairish,' I said. 'Why?'

Bob pointed towards the grating. 'Bingo,' he said. 'No knicks at all.' He waited for weeks for a return visit, but he was unlucky. Then the rains came, the grating became a waterfall and Eric insisted that the desk was moved towards the centre of the room. He could not understand why we argued so vehemently against it and we could not truthfully tell him. We knew that he would be shocked and probably embarrassed and the matter was finally let drop. When the sun came out again we made a half-hearted attempt to resume the game but the high point had already been passed.

Claire went away on holiday with her family and I stayed behind in Epsom. I had plenty to do. There were poems to revise and books to read and I was not unhappy to be on my own. I had known Claire for almost a year and while we were the best of friends and lovers I was never in doubt where her priorities lay. Her children and her husband came first. I was not just a diversion, but an extension to her life; but it was one which I knew she could and would eventually do without.

Peter and I built a tree house in the grounds of the school and sat beneath a canopy of leaves planning the future. His application for a place at university had been turned down and he now intended to revolutionise the advertising business. I saw no reason why he should not succeed. As a writer, photographer and artist he already seemed over-qualified, and his skill in manipulating whatever establishment thought it controlled him was a hidden asset which he could realise when the time was right.

'All I need is to get my foot in,' he said. 'Just wait and see.'

'What about the plays?'

'I shall go on with them,' said Peter. 'I've not yet decided about the books.'

He had recently abandoned work on a novel of suburbia entitled *Hell With a Red Roof* and passed the manuscript to me with the suggestion that I should continue where he had left off. 'It's more your style,' he explained.

'But it's your idea.'

He sighed as if I was being obtuse. 'I've got plenty of ideas. What we must decide is who's best equipped to develop them.'

'I've got my own stuff to write.'

'We have to treat ideas as common property,' said Peter, with what sounded like dwindling patience. 'If they can be made to work it doesn't matter whose name goes on the bottom.'

'To me it does,' I said.

Perched in the tree, with the sunlight brindling the beard he had started to grow, he abandoned the argument. 'I shall probably go on with the new novel,' he announced. 'I've just hit on a useful bit of research.'

One skein of the plot concerned an archery competition and Peter had found a description of how a cross-bow was made from a block of lemon wood. 'The trouble is,' he said, 'I should really try to make it myself before I write about it.'

I did not reply. I had long ago learned that Peter's enthusiasm for a project grew in inverse ratio to the problems it presented. In theory he saw no reason why he could not instantly learn how to make paper, or build a kite, or design a coracle. And, because he was ingenious and persistent, he frequently succeeded against sizeable odds. But his failures were painful for all concerned and after sharing several of his disappointments I preferred to watch rather than share the responsibility. Silence committed me to nothing.

The tree house was perhaps twenty feet above the ground and from the path below us we could not be seen. The local drama group used the school for their rehearsals and five or six of them came towards us, scripts in hand. They sat at the foot of the tree and their voices floated up through the leaves. It seemed tactless to interrupt and we listened without stirring until the rehearsal came to an end. Then we applauded.

'All right, show yourselves,' called a girl wearing a green necklace. And I lowered the rope ladder, climbed down it and met my future wife. Her name was Stella and she had one of the leading roles in the play. It was Norman Nicholson's *Old Man of the Mountains*.

'A bit boring isn't it?' I ventured.

'Not in the least,' she said.

'If it's verse drama I prefer Eliot,' said Peter.

Stella nodded. 'We did *The Family Reunion* last year. But there's nothing wrong with this. It's just different.'

She was quiet, positive and wholly unimpressed by our opinions. Her hair was short and dark. She had a broad, pleasant face and strong, white teeth. Her colour was high and her legs were trim. She was excellent company. During the next few weeks we met often and when Claire returned from holiday I told her – barely believing it myself – that Stella and I planned to be married.

Her eyes opened wide. She drew a deep breath, then kissed me soundly. 'Well darling,' she said. 'We'd better have a party.'

Stella and I were married at Epsom Registry Office in September with Peter Stanford acting as my best man. We were painfully short of money. Stella bought her own engagement ring – I paid her back in instalments – and settled my overdue NUJ subscriptions when, along with the letters of congratulation came a warning that unless the cash that I owed was forthcoming I would be expelled from the union. We went to live in what the advertisement described as 'a flatlet' – one large room and a tiny kitchen – in a commuters' village near Leatherhead where our landlord was a Chinese doctor named Lee. He quarrelled incessantly with his English wife and we were awakened late one night to hear screams beneath our window. We looked out to see Mrs Lee sprinting round the garden with her husband in pursuit. The moonlight shone brightly on the bread knife he held in one hand.

Stella worked for a subscription library in London. Every morning we caught the same train and every evening I tried to write, while Stella sat with the radio turned to a whisper. At weekends I tidied the room while Stella shopped and cooked lunch. We did not own a vacuum cleaner and I brushed the carpet on my hands and knees, working in strips from the centre to the edges and keeping time to the music from a wind-up gramophone. It was an 'Alba' – the name was stamped in gold on a black box – and I had bought it in the junk-shop next to the post office. It was an extravagance, but I convinced myself that it was a necessity. We had a dozen or so records, all 78s, and the sweeping was performed either to Louis Armstrong's *Cornet Chop Suey* or Humphrey Lyttleton's *Snake Rag*. It took at least six sides to complete the carpet and on the last strip I slowed down to the tune of *Blue for Waterloo*. In the London Jazz Club it had sounded quite different I thought.

I sold the occasional freelance article. *Lloyd's List*, the shipping paper, bought a piece on stowaways. *The Daily Mirror* paid for a features idea on thefts from the railways. I wrote about the Magnolias and the Century Theatre, a revolutionary auditorium on wheels in which Ron Sly, Eric's son, was now working. We put aside enough money to see a play almost every week. At the Old Vic we sat in the gallery and watched the black cloaks of the courtiers flow like a tide across the stage to encircle Richard Burton's snappish Hamlet. We saw Donald Wolfit sprawl across the map of Asia as Tamburlaine and afterwards I read the text and failed to discover Marlowe's mighty line which Tyrone Guthrie's production ignited.

We went to see my mother, travelling on the overnight coach to arrive, chilled and yawning, in Stoke as workers on the early shift clattered along the pavement past the bus stop. It was Stella's first visit to the Potteries and I tried to imagine how she saw that raw and grimy landscape. She had been brought up in Surrey where her father was a senior civil servant and she was used to gentler prospects. The dirt of North Staffordshire astonished her. When she put out her hand, smuts covered it like petals. But beneath the soot which furred every wall she recognised shapes and profiles which I had never noticed. In Hanley she identified Georgian houses, stone-built and four-square, between the neon scribbles of shop fronts. In Burslem she admired the cobbled sweep of Swan Bank and pointed out cottages by the canal at

Longport, standing demurely behind raised iron railings.

'You've got sharper eyes than my son,' my mother told her. 'He's never seen anything round here worth tuppence. The fact is, he's never looked.'

'He's not had much chance lately,' said Stella. 'He's been away.'

'And whose fault is that?' demanded my mother, pouncing on the opportunity. 'I've begged him to come. He never even had the decency to bring you here before you were married.'

Stella took her hand. 'We're here now.'

In two days she earned my mother's unqualified approval. The unimaginable had happened. I had married a wife who was gentle, personable and considerate. She had her own opinions and did not conceal them. Her diplomacy stilled disagreement. She did not argue; but while seeming to defer she changed the subject. Her make-up was discreet. She discussed matters which my mother found interesting. She was the right size and unlike Sadie whose top-heavy walk my mother still described in tones of outrage, she was the right shape.

'I like her voice, too,' my mother told me, as a final accolade. 'It doesn't make my head ache.'

It ached most of the time. She now slept downstairs and even the short walk to the kitchen had become a major expedition. She complained that she was unable to read, although she still persisted in writing weekly bulletins to the family. My marriage provided her with a new topic and fat blue envelopes, bulging with circumstantial accounts of how and where we lived, what we intended to do and how pleased she was with her daughter-in-law, crossed counties and oceans in a steady stream. The flow increased the following spring when Stella became pregnant and reached full spate when our daughter Susan was born in January.

We had been driven out of our flatlet by an invasion of mice. At night we heard them hauling bread-crusts around the floor and one morning when I shook the corn flakes into my bowl a mouse tobogganned out with the cereal. Dr Lee offered to lend us his cat. But a better offer came from Claire who suggested that, until our finances improved, we should move back to Epsom into her house. 'Be practical darlings,' she said. 'There's plenty of room and I could do with the rent.'

She now had a son named John who was born three months after Susan and for the next two years they grew up together. My writing table was in a turret room which overlooked the garden and I worked on stories and my poems as I watched the children progress from crawling to running round the lawn below. My own rate of development seemed much more gradual, but at last I was moving forward. My poems were now appearing in the weeklies. I regularly reviewed books, which I then promptly sold. And in one extraordinary month I had stories published by *Razzle* – a girlie magazine which specialised in risqué cartoons – and *The London Magazine* which was edited by John Lehmann.

He invited me to a party in Kensington. In the middle of one room the critic John Hayward held court in his wheelchair and I found myself skulking behind a row of potted plants from where I could watch unobserved. I was too shy to introduce myself to anyone. It was not like a little magazine party where all the guests were on equal terms. There were famous faces on all sides and without a reputation I felt naked. A man wearing a check shirt clinked his glass against mine. 'What do you suppose this is?' he asked.

'Just wine,' I said.

He sipped from the glass and then emptied it into one of the potted plants. 'Gnat's piss,' he said firmly. 'Brewed for poor poets.'

We shook hands and I learned that my companion was John Wain. The previous year he had done well with his first novel, *Hurry On Down*. But I knew him, if only through correspondence, as the editor of *First Reading*, an arts magazine broadcast on the Third Programme for which he had just accepted a number of my poems.

I thanked him but he shook his head. 'You're a local lad,' he said. 'But I took them because I liked them.'

John came from the Potteries. His father was the dentist who had pulled my first teeth. It was a remarkable coincidence, I thought, but not one which was likely to promote fellow feeling. 'Have you been back lately?' he enquired.

'Last month.'

'What was it like?'

'The same as always.'

He glanced round the room with an expression of utter distaste for the people and the place. Then he reconsidered. 'Stoke-on-Trent,' he said bleakly. 'Ah well. We should count our blessings. At least we're not there.'

He was a lecturer at Reading University where he was editing a series of books of new poetry, produced by the university's printing school. So far the list included Mari McInnes, Elizabeth Jennings and himself. He invited me to send him a larger selection of my poems which he would consider as the next book in the series. 'No promises,' he said. 'We might go broke before it happens. But we'll see.'

I sent the poems and did my best to forget about them. It was easier than I had expected. We were trying to buy a house in the neighbouring village of Bletchingley and negotiations which, for months, had barely stirred suddenly began to throb like a boil. There was a dispute over boundaries. There was not enough cash. The vendor tried to withdraw from the sale. We lay awake adding up columns of imaginary figures and the total always came to less than we required. We argued and we begged and, gravely doubting, the building society at last conceded that a mortgage might be arranged. I sat in a solicitor's office in Theobald's Road and signed an agreement between Felix McCredy, Gentleman and Philip Oakes, Journalist and wondered whether it was that mysterious distinction which had inspired the difficulties in the first place. Money alone seemed a poor excuse for the panic and uncertainty which had beset us for so long.

We moved in while the builders were still at work on the renovation. The paint was still wet on the bedroom door and we ate breakfast, ankle-deep in wood shavings. I met the postman at the gate and picked out the letter with the Reading postmark. It contained the good news I had not allowed myself to anticipate. The university was going to publish my poems. The book would be called *Unlucky Jonah*.

Eleven

THE REVIEWS were friendly. In *The Listener*, James Reeves said that the book contained 'a handful of the best poems to have been published since the war,' and my own contemporaries, including Anthony Hartley in *The Spectator* and Arthur Boyars in *Truth*, were just as generous.

I had always been contemptuous of what I believed to be an old boys' network of writers and critics who boosted each other's reputations and ignored outsiders. But now I realised that the situation was less simple than I had supposed. As Literary Editor of *The Spectator*, Anthony Hartley had not only published a number of my poems in the magazine, he had also urged me to put myself forward as a writer for *Truth*. The connection was innocent, but as I read the reviews I understood how conspiracies began.

Truth was a political weekly on the same lines as *The Spectator*, *The New Statesman* and *Time & Tide*; but it was one about which I knew very little. 'It's trying to live down its past,' said Hartley, a trifle cryptically, I thought.

'What sort of past?'

'The usual.'

Tony Hartley loved a mystery. He was currently pinning the wheels to a literary bandwagon, to be known as The Movement, on which a group of writers designated by him would carve bloody tracks through the more traditional ranks of the establishment. He saw it as a secret weapon whose passengers – a mixed bunch including D.J. Enright, Kingsley Amis, Robert Conquest and myself – shared some stylistic similarities, but had little else in common. The Movement's progress was charted in *The Spectator*. There was no overall plan of campaign. After an opening manifesto which left no one much the wiser, there had been occasional skirmishes which had ruffled the supporters of Edith Sitwell and Dylan Thomas. But the Redbrick revolution which was supposed to lead the way back to form and poetic discipline seemed to me to be already running out of steam.

Hartley was its Kropotkin, slight and bespectacled, with a talent for mischief which passed for academic purpose. I knew him very slightly; his letters to me were friendly but formal. But he made no attempt to disguise his glee when a malicious paragraph in the magazine irritated some venerable elder. And when we met now and then for a drink he would hint at great plans afoot to create further embarrassment and upset. He would never supply details and I was reminded of the anarchist in the *Daily Mirror*'s Pip, Squeak and Wilfred cartoon strip who scurried through each adventure with a bomb, its fuse already lit, tucked under his cloak.

Why he should know the secret history of *Truth* I could not imagine; but I was intrigued: I bought it for a month and was none the wiser. It was similar to the other weeklies. Its politics were conservative. It contained a larger City section than usual. But, apart from being more cheekily and abrasively written than its competitors, I thought its mixture of middles, books and the arts in no way unusual.

I submitted two articles – one about a return visit to the Potteries, the other about the workings of a magistrates' court – and they were both accepted. George Scott, the Editor, asked me to go and see him and the following week I called at his office. It was in Carteret Street in Westminster. In the reception area, behind a counter, a man and a woman were wrapping stacks of the magazine in brown paper. I was shown up a narrow staircase whose treads were trimmed with brass and led by a secretary into a room with large and grimy windows and an Axminster carpet on the floor. There was a fire burning in the grate and above it a mirror whose glass was tarnished to the colour and complexion of tortoiseshell. A *chaise longue* was aligned with one wall and facing it was a leather-topped desk and a scattering of worn leather chairs. It was a crisp autumn day and the sun was shining. But the room smelled of fog, cigar smoke and old books as if it had not been aired since the last century.

George Scott shook my hand and waved me into a chair. He was tall and slim and held his head tilted back at a slight angle as if someone behind him was holding on to his hair. His eyes were tired and when he smiled only the lower half of his face moved. His cheek-bones were welted like those of a club fighter. He looked welcoming but watchful.

'I liked the articles,' he said. 'We could do with more like that. I want to build up the reportage. Are you interested?

I told him that I was, but I wanted to write about books too.

'Anyone can be a critic,' said George. 'What I need is someone who goes out and about in the real world. You didn't go to university did you?' I shook my head and he nodded as if he had proved a point. 'It shows. In the best way, I mean. There's nothing between you and what you're writing about. You've got the right approach.' He leaned forward as if what he was about to say was highly confidential. 'Are you M.I.F.?' he asked.

'What's that?'

'Milk In First,' said George. 'I have a theory that all the best reporters put milk in before the tea. It separates Us from Them. *We* know about the real world. *They* don't.'

The proposition was new to me, but when I considered it I thought it made as much sense as most other social distinctions. 'What if you don't take milk?' I asked.

'Irrelevant. It's the attitude that matters.'

George, I learned, had been to Oxford after wartime service in the navy. He came from Middlesbrough where he had played for the Reserves and occasionally he regret-

ted that he had not pursued a career in football. It was
not a serious complaint. George had always known precisely where he was going. He worked as a journalist
on local papers, then for the *Daily Express* where he became personal assistant to Lord Beaverbrook. 'Ah yaas,'
he said, in what I divined was a Beaverbrook accent.
'A very remarkable man.'

'But wicked.'

'Speak only of what ye know,' said George. 'That's
what he'd say. And then tell you chapter and verse.'
He shook his head at the memory. 'Get to know him
if you can. You won't be sorry.'

I told him what Tony Hartley had said about *Truth*
and asked him in what way it was trying to live down
its past.

'It depends what part of the past he's talking about,'
said George. 'Henry Labouchère founded the magazine
in 1877. He was a Liberal MP and he ran a muckraking
paper in the best tradition. No one could shut him up.
He blew the gaff on everything from political graft to
the baccarat scandal when the Prince of Wales was involved in a crooked game. But those were the great days.
Things started to go badly in the thirties. The magazine
veered more and more to the Right and finished up as
a platform for fascists. It was very nasty indeed. The
really surprising thing is that no one went to jail.'

'And now?'

'And now it's a clean sheet,' said George. *Truth* had
been purchased by an accountant-publisher named
Ronald Staples and he had been given complete editorial
freedom.'

'Political as well?'

He shifted comfortably in his chair. 'Mr Staples is a
progressive Tory. Politically, we work within those para-
meters. Outside them we say what we like.' It was almost
true, although George's uncertain taste was sometimes
responsible for acts of censorship. But he was sincere
in his intentions. He could not afford to pay much,
but all his contributors were guaranteed freedom of

expression. The decision had been forced on him by economic necessity, but it was the magazine's prime virtue. Writers were attracted to *Truth* because they knew that within its pages they could speak out. It seemed to me that *Truth* was succeeding very well in living down its past.

George's deputy was Bernard Levin who, I realised, I had mistaken for the office boy on my way up the stairs. He looked about sixteen and he was phenomenally clean, with scrubbed nails and a coil of dark hair like a bed-spring lunging from his forehead. The skin of his face was translucent, like the Coalport dish my mother would hold to the light to demonstrate its quality. His suit was dark and well-cut, with a handkerchief like an exploded white rose in the breast pocket. His shoes twinkled against the grubby carpet. His shirt was silk and his tie was patterned with tiny black and white diamonds. He might have been on his way to a wedding.

Bernard was a graduate of the LSE. For a short time he had worked as a guide on coach tours around London before joining the BBC and he had been offered a job on *Truth* principally on his merits, but also as proof that the magazine's anti-Semitism was a thing of the past. There was no subject, barring sport, on which he did not hold an opinion. He could – and did – discourse on music, literature, economics, the state of the nation, the magic of Gracie Fields, Sir Oswald Mosley, the price of tickets at Covent Garden, the charm of cities and the role of the Jewish matriarch. His own family was dominated by a formidable grandmother – and her wit and wisdom – made more quotable by Bernard, I suspected – was frequently invoked to settle arguments within the office.

His disagreements were usually with Alan Brien who worked for *Truth* three days a week and whose relish for debate was even keener than Bernard's. He reminded me of a Tartar chief with narrow, slanting eyes and a massive head which was balanced on his shoulders like a stone ball on a gate-post. He moved stiffly, as if he was afraid to dislodge it and when he typed or lit a cigarette his movements were cautious, like those of a man with his back in plaster. He had a light, rapid voice and a Geordie accent which was unemphatic except when anyone challenged statistics or quotations which, I discovered, he was entirely capable of inventing on the spot. As an adolescent on Tyneside he had been blooded in soap-box politics and, for Alan, the end justified the means. What mattered was winning the argument. He had the quickest mind I had ever encountered and the curiosity to match it.

He had been at Oxford at the same time as George after serving in the RAF as a tail-gunner and was married with twin daughters. For a time he had edited a magazine for home-movie enthusiasts, called *Mini-Kine*. But he had also worked as principal ghost for Randolph Churchill and was largely responsible for the text of a book (which bore Randolph's name) on English country houses. He reviewed films and thrillers for *Truth* as well as contributing a weekly article.

As George explained, the finances of the magazine demanded that every member of the staff should be responsible for filling at least three pages of each issue. It was the only way to ensure that the books balanced, but it also meant that, if one writer was making several appearances, a pseudonym was required. Choosing the right name was difficult. For reasons it was hard to decide, the fake by-line usually sounded either synthetic or dull. Then Alan hit on a saving formula. The best by-lines, he decreed, were compounded of a modest or colloquial first name and a classical surname. As a thriller reviewer he signed himself 'John Macaulay'. I became 'John Frost'. In other sections, new hybrids including 'Joe Gladstone' and 'James Byron' made their appearance. No other magazine, I decided, could claim such a distinguished roster of contributors.

I began to write for *Truth* regularly and three months later I joined the staff. I had warned Eric that I intended to leave the agency and on the appointed day I said my goodbyes and he made me a farewell presentation of books by Dylan Thomas inscribed 'as a small memento of a happy association.' Bob took over at Thames and I moved to Carteret Street to an office which gave me a view of Westminster rooftops and the third floor premises of the Fabian Society opposite.

I shared the office with Bernard whose working habits were, to say the least, idiosyncratic. He talked incessantly; not about the work he was doing, but always about some unrelated subject. While writing a leader on the future of British industry (a theme which preoccupied *Truth*) he might also deliver a judgement on the latest production of *The Ring* (a work which preoccupied Bernard). It was as though two parallel freeways occupied his mind, both busy with high-speed traffic and each of them independent of the other. He could sub-edit someone else's copy and, at the same time, speculate on the ingredients of a mayonnaise he had eaten the night before; or he could compile a month's expenses and simultaneously quarrel with the previous five years' estimates of rainfall in London. It was a diverting performance but I felt sometimes that I was sitting opposite two other people.

He also had a way of tearing strips of paper from the pad beside him and rolling them into pellets between his finger and thumb until they were the colour and consistency of mouse droppings. It did not go unobserved by Alan who interrupted one of Bernard's monologues to complain that it was a disgusting habit. Bernard deviated for not more than three seconds. 'Don't be absurd,' he said, and returned instantly to his chosen topic.

'Disgusting and significant,' said Alan.

'Signifying what?'

'As everyone knows,' said Alan, 'it's a symptom of anal eroticism.'

I had no idea if he was telling the truth or if he had invented the information simply to confound Bernard. Either way, it worked. For the first time since we had met, I saw Bernard falter. He was not convinced, just as he knew that in his random reading Alan could have hit on some piece of research which he would expound and analyse until it was squeezed dry of its last baleful implication.

'Trust you,' he said. 'Besotted by the unpleasant.'

Alan smiled blandly. 'Not at all. I was merely pointing something out.'

'Something specious.'

'Look it up,' said Alan. 'Don't take my word for it.' His happiness was complete. He had not only thrown Bernard off course, he had also raised doubts in all our minds as to the true significance of the paper pellets. Whenever we saw them churning between Bernard's finger-tips we would think the worst.

Later that day I asked Alan if what he had implied was true. 'Probably,' he said. 'I don't see why not.'

His powers of concentration rivalled Bernard's, but they were of a different kind. Sometimes I would travel home with him to his flat in Wimbledon. As we left the office he would frequently start to read a book on page one and continue to read it, his eyes never leaving the page, until we arrived at his own front door. My job was to act as a seeing-eye dog, piloting him across roads, through ticket barriers and on and off trains.

He believed in conserving time and effort. He hated having to search for small change and the pockets of his waistcoat were loaded, like a bandolier, with ten shilling notes which he could instantly fish out when they were required. At some stage, however, he decided to refine the system by keeping pound notes in his top pockets so that he could meet larger demands just as promptly. It worked well enough until we were crossing Hyde Park one afternoon on our way to a reception at the Dorchester and we were accosted by a beggar who asked for a hand-out. Alan was struck by our contrasting situations. The park was cold and desolate; there was rain in the wind. Ahead of us lay the Dorchester with its waiting trays of free food and drink. He dipped into his waistcoat and conscience money changed hands. It was a satisfying gesture until, half an hour later, he realised that he had reached into the wrong pocket. 'I know it's only ten shilling's difference,' he said, 'but it makes me feel such a fool.' He glowered at the smoked salmon sandwiches and the hump-backed rows of angels on horseback. 'If he's still there,' he pondered, 'd'you think I could ask him for half of it back?'

I started a feature in the magazine called On the Spot covering events, both important and trivial, which gave a flavour of life in Britain in the 1950s. Usually I aimed for six to eight items. An average week's bill might include an interview with a pop star (I saw Johnny Ray in his dressing room at the London Palladium where he told me of his Red Indian ancestry); a visit to a coalfield (where a new technique of packing derelict seams with rubble had been discovered); a political luncheon (where I learned that everything I had heard about the hats worn by Tory ladies was true); a cheese tasting in Salford (where Brie and Camembert were denounced as effete and unpatriotic) and a conversation with old woodcarvers (who revered Grinling Gibbons and warned me that within a decade there would be no reserves left of English oak). To begin with I covered most of the items myself, but as On the Spot expanded I looked for more writers.

A housewife from Richmond named Monica Furlong who had sent in an unsolicited and poignant account of a refugee's Christmas became a contributor. So did John Bowen, an advertising copywriter, who made his debut by covering a bodybuilders' convention. Specialist writers, frustrated by lack of space in their own papers, wrote about sport and science and business. After three months, On the Spot had an irregular reporting team of more than a dozen. It was as though we had sunk a shaft into contemporary life and on every level we could see fossils in the making. An American efficiency expert named John Diebold forecast a revolution in something he called computers. The train drivers went on strike and at their union headquarters I was shown a model locomotive in a glass case. 'Like us,' said my guide, 'it's not working.' There were race riots in Brixton and a man with hair like strands of tarry rope told me that he dreamed of fire and blood. There was a presentation of the commercials which, within the coming year, would be screened on the new ITV network, and in a private cinema an audience of journalists jeered at the antics of an animated orange. They were all disparaging. It would never catch on, they said.

We went to press on Wednesdays. Bernard and I spent the afternoon and evening at the printer's in West London, marking galleys and correcting pages, and we rarely finished before ten o'clock at night. It was an old-fashioned establishment. Much of the typesetting was done by hand and each page was assembled on a tray with two raised metal rims. The advertising blocks and columns of type were boxed in with rules which were then secured by string. It was a slow and laborious process and one which was conducted in strict accordance with union rules.

I was in awe of the printers, whose craft seemed to me not only arcane but dangerous, involving hot metal and machinery which could split fingers like kindling. But Bernard was not impressed. With his shirt cuffs daintily hoisted by elasticated arm-bands, he picked and probed over the unfinished pages, rewriting headings, measuring cuts and sometimes, when no one was looking, rearranging the lay-outs.

'I've already told you, Bernard,' said the head printer, whose name was Mr Counsell. 'Don't touch.'

'I was saving time,' said Bernard. 'It doesn't need an expert to move a block from here to there.'

'It needs a compositor,' said Mr Counsell. 'It's not your job. You'll have 'em all out if you're not careful.'

It was not an idle threat. Bernard was tolerated and generally liked by most of the printers who regarded him as an eccentric dandy, who dared the dirt because it was his duty to do so. He was not permitted to meddle.

If he broke the rules, there were penalties to pay.

Bernard waited until Mr Counsell had gone to the far end of the print shop before returning to the page he was attempting to remake. It was lying at the wrong angle on the bench and he turned it slightly to give himself better access. It was still not satisfactory and he lifted the tray with a jerk. The string securing it snapped like cotton. The supporting rules sprang away and the type itself showered over the floor.

There was a moment's silence and then, from one end of the shop to the other, a cry went up like the baying of a lynch mob. 'Printer's pie!' they shouted. 'Printer's pie!'

Mr Counsell strolled slowly to the scene of the disaster. 'That means drinks all round,' he said.

If anything, the incident enhanced Bernard's reputation. He rose to the occasion magnificently and work was halted while bottles circulated and ritual toasts were drunk. It cost him, he estimated, around £20, which was as much as I earned in a week. But it was cheap at the price, Mr Counsell assured him. 'We've never had a printer's pie down here before,' he said. 'You could say you've made history.'

When we changed printers the story travelled ahead of us and I realised, not for the first time, how each trade and profession distorted its traditions. Who we were and what we did became the stuff of anecdote, applied like varnish to a portrait. The true likeness was disguised and what we loved was caricature. Working at *Truth* it was inevitable. There was no doubt that our founder, Henry Labouchère, had been an astute politician and a courageous journalist. But he was also a notorious ladies' man who, it was claimed, had seduced the wives of many of his fellow MPs. The office had been his place of assignation. There was a private staircase which led to a street door some way from the main entrance and it was easy to imagine the meetings that had taken place while the fire sulked in the grate and the fog pressed against the windows. The *chaise longue* that stood opposite George's desk had been there in Labouchère's time and we examined it for stains and tears which would give credence to the legend. A nick in the leather might have been caused by a nail or a bracelet which had scored the upholstery. A loose button could have been dislodged by glacé-kid boots, scrabbling beneath the broadcloth-covered flanks of our distinguished predecessor.

I felt sometimes that I belonged to a club and that the staff and contributors to the magazine were its members. There were editorial conferences two or three times a week and sitting in the fug of a February afternoon with the windows tightly closed and the door sealed against draughts, there seemed little connection with the world outside. I spent hours in front of the mirror, with Alan instructing me over one shoulder and Bernard advising me over the other, learning precisely how to knot a bow tie. Once a month I sold my review copies to Mr Franks of Gastons who called at the private entrance to collect the books in a plain van, and on the proceeds we lunched at Overtons in Victoria. In the first floor dining room, as narrow as a railway coach, we ate whitebait and Dover sole and afterwards we walked back to the office through St James's Park. Beside the lake, the pelicans flapped their apricot pouches and behind them the turrets and domes of Westminster reared into the winter sky. I savoured an almost reckless sense of privilege.

Others were less lucky. The translator and biographer, Margaret Crosland, had asked me if I could put some reviewing in the way of a friend of hers, a Canadian writer named Norman Levine. He was living in a rented cottage in St Ives with his wife and children and we arranged to meet when he was next in London. Without warning, he turned up at the office and I took him for a drink in the pub round the corner. He was short and stocky, with a broken front tooth and stubble glinting along the line of his jaw. His shirt collar was grimy and he looked tired.

'I hitched up from Cornwall,' he said. 'It took longer than I expected.'

He could not stay long because he was going to have lunch with Nancy Spain, who was then an influential book reviewer on the *Daily Express*. Norman had just published his first novel, *The Angled Road*, and his fellow Canadian, Lord Beaverbrook, had ordered a show of interest. 'I'm not happy about it,' said Norman. 'I can't stand the *Express*.'

'You don't have to,' I said. 'It doesn't matter.'

He scrubbed his jaw unhappily. 'Somehow it doesn't seem right.'

He had practically no money, he told me; but he would not accept a loan. I commissioned two book reviews and saw him on his way to Scott's Oyster Bar in Piccadilly where he had been instructed to meet Nancy Spain. Weeks later, when he next came to London, he described what had taken place.

'She was crazy about the book,' he said. 'But what she liked even better was the fact that I was broke. I sat there among all those white table-cloths and pink lampshades and told her how I'd hitched to London because I had no cash and how I'd spent my money buying food for the children. She told me to write the story down just as I'd told it to her and the *Express* would pay me £50. Cash on the nail. Then she took me back to her flat and sat me in front of a typewriter with a bottle of whisky and left me to it.'

He was left alone for five hours. Nancy Spain went out to the theatre and, fuelled by whisky, he tried to give an account of what it was like to be a hungry writer with a family to feed. 'I really tried,' said Norman. 'I thought of that £50 and what I could do with it. But the harder I tried, the more certain I became that the experience was too important for a newspaper article. I had to save it for a story of my own. I filled up the wastepaper basket and then I watched it spill over on to the floor. I spoiled page after page, but the words wouldn't flow. Nancy Spain came back to an empty whisky bottle and no story. We said goodbye and I hitched my way back to Cornwall.'

I was deeply impressed. But when I repeated the tale to Alan he was indignant. 'What about his wife? What about his children?' he demanded. 'They're more important than his integrity.'

'He felt he was selling out.'

'Nonsense,' said Alan. 'In any case, he's given himself another story now.'

I liked Norman, but his conscience – which scanned not only his own moral dilemmas, but those of his friends – was less easy to tolerate. He was convinced that, as a poet, I spent too much time on journalism and frequently told me so.

'But I enjoy being a journalist,' I said.

'I know you have to say that.'

'I mean it,' I said. 'I like the life and I need the money.'

'Ah,' said Norman. 'The money. How much exactly do you need?'

He believed that I should fix on a particular sum and having once earned it, devote myself to literature. I told him it was not so simple. My estimates varied from month to month, but whatever figure I quoted Norman looked severe. His father was a Polish immigrant who had peddled fruit in downtown Ottawa and although Norman himself had been a bomber pilot during the war and graduated with distinction from McGill University, he still weighed duty against desire as scrupulously as his father might have done on scales which allowed no latitude.

His short stories were, for the most part, terse accounts of hardship stoically endured. But as Alan was prompt to point out, the hardships which he accepted as the writer's lot were also imposed on his family. 'And I don't suppose they've been given much option,' he said.

Unmistakeably, though, he was a good and serious writer. And the standards he set for others were those he conformed to himself. I suggested that he wrote an article for *Truth* about the pilchard fleet that sailed from Newlyn but on its way into print George excised one sentence describing how, before the pilchard drive began, the fishermen ritually pissed on the prow of the boat for good luck.

The censorship struck me as absurd and I said so, but George was adamant. 'I know our readers,' he said. 'They don't like that kind of language.'

'But it's necessary.'

'Not at all,' said George, measuring the proposed cut. 'You can't tell me that ten words make any difference either way.'

I tried to argue how important I thought it was to preserve the form of words that Norman had used, as carefully ordered as an incantation. But I was wasting my time. Norman was writing about magic and George was defending good taste. 'Either we make the cut or we don't print the piece,' he said.

I capitulated. The cut was made, the magazine went to press and Norman received his cheque. He would not cash it for weeks and he refused to write for us again. 'It's too risky,' he said. 'There'll come a day when I might want to describe someone peeing on a boat and I wouldn't want George losing sleep over it.'

It was an unlikely eventuality, I thought. George never agonised over any decision, right or wrong. He believed himself, with some justification, to be a defender of free speech. But while he supported the principle, he sometimes wavered on the terminology. Free speech was not the same thing as plain speech. What George disliked was coarseness. When he was at university he had edited a literary magazine called *Oxford Opinion*. But, unlike most undergraduate publications, it had scandalised no one. In its language, at least, *Truth* was just as discreet. Sexual matters, in particular, could only be alluded to circumspectly.

We introduced a monthly page of new poetry which I edited, and while the standard was high there was never a hint of eroticism. In a long and vivid instalment of autobiography, the bran-tub into which Alan occasionally dipped when he was short of an idea to fill his prescribed number of pages, he described his purchase

of a kitchen table which had once belonged to the murderer and necrophile, John Halliday Christie. I had reported the preliminary hearings of Christie's trial and
there was no doubt that the table on which the Briens
now ate their family meals had once been put to a much
more sinister use.

'Mind you,' said Alan. 'It's been re-covered since then.'

George shuddered perceptibly. 'There's no need to go
into that.'

'People are interested in murder,' said Alan. 'It's perfectly normal.'

'I don't want to hear about it,' said George. 'Nor do
the readers.'

He looked for other ways in which to increase the
circulation. Anthony Howard, who began by reporting
for On the Spot, was called up and wrote an anonymous
series of articles fiercely critical of life in the peacetime
army. Randolph Churchill brought valuable controversy
to the pages, but his contributions were always attended,
before and after publication, by telephone calls of enormous length and complexity, which Bernard was dele-
gated to take. The plan was to bury one monologue in
another; but even Bernard was overwhelmed. For as long
as an hour at a time he would sit with the phone at
arm's-length, while at home in East Bergholt Randolph
sipped his well-watered whisky and held forth on the
responsibilities of the press and the cowardice of editors.
He ignored interjections and time pips alike. 'I will not
be intimidated,' he declared. 'The telephone is merely
an instrument of communication.'

The magazine was redesigned with a blue and white
cover and a new type face. We experimented with line
drawings by Bill Hewison and Peter Kneebone and tried
out a cartoonist named Peter Shaffer. George increased
the sports coverage and in a bid to attract more advertising from the City we embarked on a series of articles
by leading businessmen, whose visions of a brave new
commercial world were remarkable only for their mani-
fest faith in the Conservative party and a prose style

which made all our tomorrows sound simultaneously ominous and dull. I actually fell asleep while I was punctuating the manifesto submitted by a cement tycoon named Sir Halford Reddish and for years afterwards his name was synonymous for me for all that was boring.

Whatever we tried, the circulation did not respond for long. It fluttered upwards and then fell back. For a while it meandered along a disappointingly low level, then settled into a decline which seemed to be irreversible. It was an absurd situation; we were able to impress everyone but the readers we so badly wanted. Not a week went by without a flattering reference to the magazine or its editor (usually described as 'young and brilliant') in the *Evening Standard* Diary or some other column. And our weekly table of contents which blazoned the names of contributors across the front page was a useful advertisement which resulted in our best writers being picked off by rival papers just as they were beginning to win the following we needed ourselves.

That spring brought a reprieve. There was a newspaper strike and overnight every news-stand and bookstall was bare of newsprint. Without a daily paper to while away their travelling time, commuters read anything that came to hand. Libraries reported an upsurge in borrowing. Shops were stripped of paperbacks. On Victoria Station I saw a man deeply engrossed in a knitting pattern. For the weeklies it was business as usual and we quadrupled our print order and sales. For the first time we ran a news diary with pages of photographs. At the same time, said George, it was vital that we retained enough of our regular features to demonstrate what the magazine had to offer when times were normal.

A few subscriptions trickled in, but although we did well enough on the street – where, at a glance, our billboards seemed to advertise an evangelical rally – the long-term prospects appeared dim. *Truth* was now printed in Rochester and as Bernard and I travelled to that dreary town and looked out over the mud-flats flanking the estuary it was hard to guess what we would be doing in a year's time. I was writing a novel and – like everyone else on the magazine – I had received overtures from editors and feature editors around Fleet Street who had caught the appetizing whiff of new talent in the air. Soon, they suspected, it would be on the open market. And, although they were at pains to stress that they had nothing positive or permanent to offer and that they would do nothing to undermine the loyalty that George commanded from his staff, they hinted that it would be just as well to keep in touch. Clearly they did not expect *Truth* to survive.

'It may never happen,' said Bernard.

'You don't believe that.'

'Our proprietor is an accountant,' he said. 'He would also like to be a Sir. While we can be of help in that direction and it doesn't cost him too much, I imagine we shall stay in business.'

'What will you do?'

'I shall wait and see,' he said. 'I live in hope.'

The hopes which had begun with the newspaper strike were laid to rest the following week when Fleet Street went back to work. Unsold copies of *Truth* were stacked high in the front office and I caught myself tip-toeing past them as if they were bodies awaiting burial. My own name was on the front cover, repeated a thousand times beneath the brown paper wrapping, and I thought regretfully of all the potential readers who would never see it.

We met for the morning conference and George looked up from a typed memorandum which sat squarely on his blotter. 'To begin with,' he said, 'I propose to review our plans for the next twelve months.' He sounded confident and positive and for a moment I forgot the remaindered copies below us on their way back to pulp. I thought of Labouchère and his successful muckraking and the ladies he had entertained on the *chaise longue*. Times had changed. The club was winding down; but for the time being it was business as usual. George lit a cigar and blew the smoke at the tarnished mirror. Then he passed round the box. We were going out in style.

Twelve

MY MOTHER complained that the print was too small for her to read any of my articles in *Truth*. 'Not that I'd understand them,' she wrote. 'We live in different worlds.'

The reproach was a familiar one, but it still stung; not least because it was true. My mother's world had been reduced to a room in a nursing home at Newcastle-under-Lyme. It was partly financed by a teachers' pension fund to which she had subscribed all her working life and all its residents were former teachers. 'But we have nothing in common,' said my mother. 'They're not my sort.'

She meant they were not her family. Beside her bed she kept a large blue and gilt box which had once contained writing paper. Now it was filled to the brim with photographs. They were in no particular order. There were portraits of her parents taken fifty years earlier; snapshots of me in my pram and in the army; a picture of my mother in nurse's uniform and a sepia print of a Sunday school outing, in which girls wearing hats like wedges of puff-pastry sat beneath the extended branch of a giant yew along which young men in stiff collars had positioned themselves, grinning nervously into the vanished sunlight. There were photographs of my Uncle Ernest exhibiting his prize dahlias; several of my Aunt Jenny in the garden of her house on High Lane; and one of my Uncle Joe, taken on a boat trip in America in 1913. He stood between two friends, his straw hat tilted to one side as if it was on a hinge. 'Three Shriners on a Spree' said the message on the back.

They were my mother's family archives. She would

empty the box on to her bed and stir the photographs, old and new, as if by arranging them into a sequence which she had yet to learn she could bring them to life. Beside the box was her autograph album. Most of the entries were inspirational: 'Hope is the one infallible physician'; 'Angels do not toil: they let their good works grow out of them'; 'When your life touches another life, there you have opportunity'. As a child, I had thought of them as bulletins from the beyond. The sentiments were so noble, their meaning so profound that I could not imagine them being uttered by mortals. I preferred the sketches and watercolours, most of them done by artists who had designed the patterns on the pottery sold by my father's firm. There were garlands of pink roses, a Pomeranian dog, a Highlander wearing a tam 'o shanter and an Egyptian slave girl whose bare breasts were innocent of nipples. Best of all, in the centre of one page, there was a penny stamp bearing the head of Edward VII and the inscription 'By gum it's stuck!' For years I had tried to persuade my mother to let me have it for my own collection, but she invariably refused. Now I understood why. She turned the pages, sometimes not even bothering to look at them. Her fingers rested on the illustrations and traced the signatures: 'Zillah. Oct 1905'; 'F. Price. Oct 1906'; 'George Wade Poxon. Trenton, New Jersey. U.S.A. Sep 14 1911.' She was touching past happiness and she needed all that she could find.

The crisis had come to a head the previous winter when a cold which my mother was unable to shake off turned to pneumonia. Within the same week Mary Evans was warned that her shortness of breath, which my mother had always blamed on over-eating, indicated a heart condition. They both needed nursing, but an influenza epidemic as virulent as the plague swept through North Staffordshire and all would-be helpers were driven to their beds. I was sent for and travelled north through blizzards and over roads glazed with black ice; but by the time I arrived my mother had been taken to hospital. Her bed in the dining room was soon occupied by Stella who joined me after leaving our daughter in the care of her parents, but almost immediately collapsed with gastric flu. With two sick women to look after and my mother to visit, I was in despair. I told my troubles to Mr Jolley who ran the greengrocer's shop at the top of the avenue and he nodded reflectively. 'Tha'll know tha's been here, then,' he said.

I could not be so philosophical. The journey to and from the hospital took over four hours. Buses were infrequent and snow tumbled from a pale sky. In the middle of a long ward my mother sat propped up in bed, an unread paper by her side. She still had a high temperature and there was a bright patch of colour on either cheek. 'Are you feeding the birds?' she asked abruptly.

'When there's time.'

'They get fed twice a day,' she said. 'Not just bread. There's some suet in the pantry and a tin of old pastry. And you must chop it up into small pieces. Otherwise the starlings get it all.'

'There's more to think about than birds,' I said.

My mother gave no indication of having heard. 'They need water too. There was a man on the wireless. He said it was more important than putting out food. You won't forget?'

'I won't forget.'

I told her how Mary was and how Stella had fallen ill and how few and far between the buses were, but she was not listening. Her mind was elsewhere and I held her hand and waited. 'I've made up my mind,' she said at last. 'I'm selling the house and moving into the nursing home.'

'Are you sure?'

'Certain,' she said. 'There's nothing else for it. The sooner the better.'

For several months we had discussed the possibility of her going into the nursing home but she had resisted making a final decision. Alternatively, we had considered whether it would be feasible for her to come and live with us, but she did not want to leave the Potteries.

'If you came back up here,' she said, 'things might be different.'

'I can't do that.'

'You mean won't.'

'Can't and won't,' I said. 'I told you that years ago.'

'There's no need to remind me,' said my mother with a spurt of temper. 'You never would do what I wanted you to. You've always looked after Number One. That's all that matters to you.'

It was an argument, I thought, which would never be resolved. The rights and wrongs of it went beyond love and duty and now I had other responsibilities which, in my mother's eyes, gave me an unfair advantage. She approved of Stella and she was proud of her grand-daughter. But she resented them for the justification they provided for me to pursue my own course of action. At the same time she clung to her own independence. In her own home she could do as she wished. 'When I close my front door,' she declared, 'there's no one to give me orders.' In her narrow kingdom she was the sole ruler. But now she had abdicated.

'I won't be going back,' she said. 'I couldn't stand it. You'll have to dispose of things.'

I thought of the mahogany dining table on which she had written her letters to the family, the sea chest which her great-grandfather had taken to America and back, the bed with its mother-of-pearl inlay in which she had slept with my father. 'You must take what you want and sell the rest,' she said. 'It's up to you now.'

We did as she wished. The house and its contents were sold and Stella and I went through the empty rooms for the last time. Mary had gone to live with a cousin in the neighbouring village of Smallthorne, but she came to see that we had left everything in good order for the new owners. She was appalled by the amount we had thrown away and spent an afternoon sorting through the contents of the dustbin, setting aside objects she could not believe we had meant to discard.

'What about this?' she asked, holding up a china lady

wearing a poke bonnet and a knitted woollen skirt which
was intended to cover knick-knacks on a dressing table.

'I don't like it.'

'But it's lovely,' she said. 'Mrs Royals brought it back
from Bournemouth for your mother three years ago.'

'She never used it.'

'She was keeping it for best,' said Mary. Throughout
the afternoon her pile of salvage mounted. There was
a sauce-boat which I had always loathed; cups and saucers, most of them cracked, but still serviceable; a picture
frame studded with sea shells; a mock leather binder
for the Radio Times. As each unlovely item was reclaimed
I saw it in the context of my own life. Nothing fitted;
what my mother had regarded as precious was of no
use to me. I felt that I should apologise, but I did not
know what for. I wished that I had sealed the lid of
the dustbin or arranged for its early collection. Now it
was too late. My crime had been revealed.

'You're surely not throwing this away,' said Mary,
holding up a glass in a chromium holder.

'I've no use for it.'

'There's always use for a glass,' she said. 'And the
holder's lovely.'

I shook my head. 'I haven't got room.'

'Your mother had hot drinks in it,' said Mary. She
showed me the holder, as though explaining its purpose
to a child. 'It saves you from burning your fingers.'

'I can see that. I still don't want it.'

Mary pursed her lips and added it to her pile. I realised
that I had offended her, so badly as it turned out that
she felt driven to describe my rejection of the glass to
one of my cousins who promptly told my mother, who
was furious. I was accused of ungraciousness, insensitiv-
ity and plain snobbishness. 'I suppose,' said my mother,
'that it's not good enough for Epsom.'

'I just don't need it.'

'Indeed,' she said. 'And what else have you decided
you don't need?'

I hardly dared tell her. The best of the furniture had

been bought by John Witcomb, a friend from the avenue who was soon to be married. I did not want the three-piece bedroom suite, or the chairs upholstered in uncut moquette, or the oak sideboard whose corner had always bruised my hip when I hurried into the dining room. John was glad of them and I thought my mother – who admired his determination to qualify as a teacher – would be pleased to know they had gone to a good home. It was not so.

'I suppose none of it's good enough for Epsom,' she said.

It was a phrase with which she was to belabour me for the rest of her life, long after we moved elsewhere. She was contemptuous of the few things I had chosen to take; a carpet, a wooden chest, some bedroom chairs and the kitchen dresser in which my father had kept his woodworking tools. I had learned to stand and then walk by holding on to the bottom drawer. It had a place among my happier memories. 'That old thing,' said my mother. 'What do you want with that? It's not worth tuppence.'

The truth was that nothing in the house had been of great value. Possessions which my mother had prized from the earliest days of her marriage went for a few shillings. I felt insulted on her behalf. But, unwittingly, I had added to the insult. I wished that I had claimed the glass in the chrome holder as an heirloom. But now the damage was done. It was not good enough for Epsom and I was not allowed to forget it.

My mother moved directly from hospital to the nursing home. Its name was Victoria House and it stood behind ramparts of privet, with a large garden to the rear. It lay on the other side of the Potteries to High Lane where my mother had lived for the past thirty years and although it was no more than eight or ten miles away, she felt she was in a foreign country. Everything was different, she said. Not even the tea tasted the same, although it was served in her own cup of bone china with a gold clover leaf stamped on one side. She slept badly and sometimes woke wondering where she was. Because space was limited she was at first given a bed in the general ward where she could not switch on the light for fear of disturbing other residents. There was a small, uncurtained window at one end of the ward where she watched for the first signs of dawn and when she described her vigil I was reminded of immigrants to Australia, bemused by their first glimpse of unfamiliar stars. There was no Southern Cross in my mother's night sky, but the constellations were just as strange. After years of living with only one companion she was confused by the presence of so many other people. 'I hate it,' she said. 'I'll never get used to it.' She tried not to complain. As she so often repeated, she did not want to be a nuisance. It was her duty, she felt, to put a brave face on it. But it took all her courage and sometimes it faltered. When it did, she became querulous and demanding. She sulked ('Just like she did when she was a girl,' said my Aunt Ada) and instead of talking to the visitors who came to see her in relays so that she had constant company, she would sit and glare at the bed opposite. Fortunately it was occupied by a blind lady who was unaware of my mother's displeasure. Even if she had been, she would have taken it in her stride. 'She's a cut above the rest of them here,' my mother reported later. 'She had a big house, full of antique furniture. She must miss it dreadfully.' As always, when there was someone for whom she could feel sorry she cheered up wonderfully. And when she was allocated a bed in a room with only one other person – a former headmistress who was both elderly and unmarried – her spirits rose by several more degrees.

Her room-mate was named Miss Cobb. She seemed to have no relatives and few people came to see her, a circumstance which made her an object of sympathy. But this was offset by the fact that she was fit enough to attend a weekly service at a church close by Victoria

House. My mother tried hard not to mind, but she became intensely jealous of the outings. Bed-bound, she saw herself as a prisoner unjustly confined. There was no one to blame, but this only made the situation harder to bear. Sunday became the worst day of the week. 'She's not even chapel,' said my mother bitterly, as though the lack of parity between C of E and Methodist believers was the last straw.

Her morale was partly restored when we took Susan to see her. She was a beautiful fair haired child and her visit to Victoria House became a royal tour. Patients leaned from their beds to touch her. She was given sweets, fruit, money. As we went from room to room it was as though we were the guardians of a princess whose smile could miraculously cure illness and even old age. Some of the credit went to Stella and myself. But it was my mother, whose grand-daughter this presence was, who was accorded the greater glory. It was she who had drawn the lightning; she who had brought the blessing. My mother did not demur. Any virtues which Susan might possess were clearly inherited. 'Just look,' said my mother proudly. 'She's got the Barlow jaw. Full of character. There's no mistaking it.' The proof of continuity sustained her and I sometimes regretted that she did not know her other grandchild. Emma was now teaching in Essex and she had enrolled Alice as a pupil at the same school. She too looked like a Barlow. But she had another name, another life. It was too late for revelations.

Over the next year my mother's health worsened. She was in constant pain and for much of the time she was under heavy sedation. Nevertheless she wrote to me two or three times a week. I did not look forward to her letters. 'I have nothing new to tell you,' she would write. 'Only that I am sick of this room, this place, this existence.' But there was no remedy for what tormented her; nor was there any consolation. She filled page after page with charges and recriminations, some of them going back ten or fifteen years. I was familiar with them all.

I had endured them and I had answered them. But I could no longer respond. The dialogue was exhausted.

Physically, she seemed to fade like one of the photographs that she spread over her counterpane. Sometimes I saw her studying a thirty or forty year old image of herself as if she found it difficult to reconcile her memory of the woman she had been with the woman she had become. She would stroke her hair with an ebony-backed brush, embossed with her initials and look almost shyly at her reflection in the hand mirror which my father had given to her when they were first married. The mirror was made of silver. It had an art nouveau pattern on the back of two cranes standing with their beaks raised, among bull-rushes and lily pads. Once she threw the mirror on to the floor. I thought she had dropped it but when I gave it back to her she turned it face downwards. 'I can't stand the sight of myself,' she said.

What she saw was not what she wanted to see. But although her hair was no longer the glossy black bob it had been when she was young, it was still trim and well tended. Her skin was still fine and her eyes were the same misty blue that had always reminded me of a girl on a song sheet. What had drained away was her authority. She could still command love and attention. But because it was given to her as matter-of-factly as clean sheets or afternoon tea, which were available to all the residents of the nursing home, she saw nothing remarkable in the concern. It was not exclusively for her. It was everyone's entitlement and as such it did not interest her.

We both made an effort not to quarrel. I visited her as often as I could, but it was not as frequently as she would have wished. 'If only you were closer,' she said again and again. 'We have so much time to make up.' She made an effort to read my poems, but they did not hold her attention. 'To tell you the truth,' she said, 'I never really got on with poetry. Not even Tennyson.' I offered to read them aloud to her, but she refused. 'It's not the sort you can say aloud.'

'Why not?'

'It's private,' said my mother. 'It was never meant for people like me.'

We had effected a kind of reconciliation, but I chose not to examine it too closely. We got on best when we did not talk, but sat listening to a concert or a variety programme on the radio while Miss Cobb tactfully found other things to do and the garden filled up with dusk and a blackbird mounted guard on his song post. When he began to sing my mother would switch off the radio and lie back on her pillow with her hands clasped on her chest. 'He's singing for me,' she would say. 'He's better than any of your bands.'

It was easy then to think of nothing but the bird-song flooding the garden and the still room in which vases and pictures glimmered against the walls. It was not like the home which my mother had given up or the one to which I would soon be returning. But it was not an unfriendly place. We did not switch on the light. We waited for darkness to occupy the neutral ground.

I was digging the garden on a late spring afternoon when the matron of Victoria House telephoned with the news that my mother had died. 'It was half an hour ago,' she said. 'I couldn't get through sooner.'

I felt only a slight surprise as if the other party in a conversation which had lasted all my life had gone away without my noticing. It seemed odd that I had not known the moment it happened. 'It doesn't matter,' I said. 'Thank you.'

'She went peacefully,' said the matron. 'It was a blessing.'

I went outside and watched the wind tug at the jasmine which covered the front of the house and my surprise gave way to relief. I was glad that my mother was dead. I was glad that she was no longer in pain. I was glad that it was over.

No trains were running because of a rail strike, but Bernard queued for hours to buy me a ticket on the coach to Stoke and I travelled up the next day. There was a service at the crematorium and afterwards the mourners assembled at my Uncle Ernest's house for high tea. My Aunt Annie served plates of sliced ham, followed by cling peaches with cream and the house filled up with the mingled essence of cologne and lavender water and tobacco smoke, just as my own home had done on Sunday evenings when my parents and their friends gathered round the piano in the front room to sing hymns.

My Uncle Ernest beckoned me into the kitchen. 'There's just a couple of things,' he said. 'Syd wants to know if he can have your father's watch.'

Syd was my step-brother who lived in Sheffield. I had stayed with him for a year when my mother went into hospital for the operation which everyone assured me had saved her life. The watch which my father had once carried in his waistcoat pocket had remained on my mother's bedside table after his death. 'He's got nothing else of your dad's,' said my uncle. 'He'd be glad of it.'

'He can have it,' I said.

My uncle nodded as though he was ticking off a list in his head. 'Right you are. Then there's your mother's ring. They took it from her finger before they closed the coffin.'

He gave it to me and I tried it on for size. It was too small for my ring finger but it fitted the little finger of my right hand. 'I'll just wear it for now,' I said.

My uncle watched me turn it this way and that. 'You mustn't feel bad.'

'I don't.'

He nodded comfortably as if he had dealt with every item on the list. 'It's best that we remember her as she was,' he said. 'Very awkward at times.'

'I loved her,' I said.

'We all did,' said my uncle. 'But she was awkward, just as she was brave. And she'd had enough. She was ready to go.' He reamed out his pipe before stuffing the bowl with shag. Then he lit it with a kitchen match. 'I was with her when she died,' he said. 'I looked out of the window for a second and when I looked back she'd slipped away. I spoke to her but she didn't answer.'

The room was filling with layer upon layer of smoke and I could not see the expression on my uncle's face, but when he squeezed my hand I knew that what he was about to tell me was important. 'I looked into her eyes,' he said. 'Her eyes were like stars.'